Taking An ASE Certification Test

This study guide will help prepare you to take the ASE test. It contains descriptions of the types of questions used on the test, the task list from which the test questions are derived, a review of the task list subject information, and a practice test containing ASE style questions.

ABOUT ASE

The National Institute for Automotive Service Excellence (ASE) is a non-profit organization founded in 1972 for the purpose of improving the quality of automotive service and repair through the voluntary testing and certification of automotive technicians. Currently, there are over 400,000 professional technicians certified by ASE in over 40 different specialist areas.

ASE certification recognizes your knowledge and experience, and since it is voluntary, taking and passing an ASE certification test also demonstrates to employers and customers your commitment to your profession. It can mean better compensation and increased employment opportunities as well.

ASE not only certifies technician competency, it also promotes the benefits of technician certification to the motoring public. Repair shops that employ at least one ASE technician can display the ASE sign. Establishments where 75% of technicians are certified, with at least one technician certified in each area of service offered by the business, are eligible for the ASE Blue Seal of Excellence program. ASE encourages consumers to patronize these shops through media campaigns and car care clinics.

To become ASE certified, you must pass at least one ASE exam and have at least two years of related work experience. Technicians that pass all tests in a series earn Master Technician status. Your certification is valid for five years, after which time you must retest to retain certification, demonstrating that you have kept up with the changing technology in the field.

THE ASE TEST

An ASE test consists of forty to eighty multiple-choice questions. Test questions are written by a panel of technical experts from vehicle, parts and equipment manufacturers, as well as working technicians and technical education instructors. All questions have been pre-tested and quality checked on a national sample of technicians. The questions are derived from information presented in the task list, which details the knowledge that a technician must have to pass an ASE test and be recognized as competent in that category. The task list is periodically updated by ASE in response to changes in vehicle technology and repair techniques.

Customer Service 1-800-240-1968
FAX 218-723-9146
e-mail www.ma@superfill.com
URL: www.motorage.com

Taking An ASE Certification Test

There are five types of questions on an ASE test:

Direct, or Completion
MOST Likely
Technician A and Technician B
EXCEPT
LEAST Likely

Direct, or Completion

This type of question is the kind that is most familiar to anyone who has taken a multiple-choice test: you must answer a direct question or complete a statement with the correct answer. There are four choices given as potential answers, but only one is correct. Sometimes the correct answer to one of these questions is clear, however in other cases more than one answer may seem to be correct. In that case, read the question carefully and choose the answer that is most correct. Here is an example of this type of test question:

A compression test shows that one cylinder is too low. A leakage test on that cylinder shows that there is excessive leakage. During the test, air could be heard coming from the tailpipe. Which of the following could be the cause?

    A. broken piston rings
    B. bad head gasket
    C. bad exhaust gasket
    D. an exhaust valve not seating

There is only one correct answer to this question, answer **D**. If an exhaust valve is not seated, air will leak from the combustion chamber by way of the valve out to the tailpipe and make an audible sound. Answer C is wrong because an exhaust gasket has nothing to do with combustion chamber sealing. Answers A and B are wrong because broken rings or a bad head gasket would have air leaking through the oil filler or coolant system.

MOST Likely

This type of question is similar to a direct question but it can be more challenging because all or some of the answers may be nearly correct. However, only one answer is the most correct. For example:

When a cylinder head with an overhead camshaft is discovered to be warped, which of the following is the **MOST** correct repair option?

    A. replace the head
    B. check for cracks, straighten the head, surface the head
    C. surface the head, then straighten it
    D. straighten the head, surface the head, check for cracks

The most correct answer is **B**. It makes no sense to perform repairs on a cylinder head that might not be useable. The head should first be checked for warpage and cracks. Therefore, answer B is more correct than answer D. The head could certainly be replaced, but the cost factor may be prohibitive and availability may be limited, so answer B is more correct than answer A. If the top of the head is warped enough to interfere with cam bore alignment and/or restrict free movement of the camshaft, the head must be straightened before it is resurfaced, so answer C is wrong.

Technician A and Technician B

These questions are the kind most commonly associated with the ASE test. With these questions you are asked to choose which technician statement is correct, or whether they both are correct or incorrect. This type of question can be difficult because very often you may find one technician's statement to be clearly correct or incorrect while the other may not be so obvious. Do you choose one technician or both? The key to answering these questions is to carefully examine each technician's statement independently and judge it on its own merit. Here is an example of this type of question.

A vehicle equipped with rack-and-pinion steering is having the front end inspected. Technician A says that the inner tie-rod ends should be inspected while in their normal running position. Technician B says that if movement is felt between the tie-rod stud and the socket while the tire is moved in and out, the inner tie-rod should be replaced. Who is correct?

    A. Technician A only
    B. Technician B only
    C. Both A and B
    D. Neither A or B

The correct answer is **C**; both technicians' statements are correct. Technician B is clearly correct because any play felt between the tie-rod stud and the socket while the tire is moved in and out indicates that the assembly is worn and requires replacement. However, Technician A is also correct because inner tie-rods should be inspected while in their normal running position, to prevent binding that may occur when the suspension is allowed to hang free.

EXCEPT

This kind of question is sometimes called a negative question because you are asked to give the incorrect answer. All of the possible answers given are correct EXCEPT one. In effect, the correct answer to the question is the one that is wrong. The word EXCEPT is always capitalized in these questions. For example:

All of the following are true of torsion bars **EXCEPT:**

    A. They can be mounted longitudinally or transversely.
    B. They serve the same function as coil springs.
    C. They are interchangeable from side-to-side.
    D. They can be used to adjust vehicle ride height.

The correct answer is **C**. Torsion bars are not normally interchangeable from side-to-side. This is because the direction of the twisting or torsion is not the same on the left and right sides. All of the other answers contain true statements regarding torsion bars.

LEAST Likely

This type of question is similar to EXCEPT in that once again you are asked to give the answer that is wrong. For example:

Blue-gray smoke comes from the exhaust of a vehicle during deceleration. Of the following, which cause is **LEAST** likely?

    A. worn valve guides
    B. broken valve seals
    C. worn piston rings
    D. clogged oil return passages

The correct answer is **C**. Worn piston rings will usually make an engine smoke worse under acceleration. All of the other causes can allow oil to be drawn through the valve guides under the high intake vacuum that occurs during deceleration.

PREPARING FOR THE ASE TEST

Begin preparing for the test by reading the task list. The task list describes the actual work performed by a technician in a particular specialty area. Each question on an ASE test is derived from a task or set of tasks in the list. Familiarizing yourself with the task list will help you to concentrate on the areas where you need to study.

The text section of this study guide contains information pertaining to each of the tasks in the task list. Reviewing this information will prepare you to take the practice test.

Take the practice test and compare your answers with the correct answer explanations. If you get an answer wrong and don't understand why, go back and read the information pertaining to that question in the text.

After reviewing the tasks and the subject information and taking the practice test, you should be prepared to take the ASE test or be aware of areas where further study is needed. When studying with this study guide or any other source of information, use the following guidelines to make sure the time spent is as productive as possible:

• Concentrate on the subject areas where you are weakest.
• Arrange your schedule to allow specific times for studying.
• Study in an area where you will not be distracted.
• Don't try to study after a full meal or when you are tired.
• Don't wait until the last minute and try to 'cram' for the test.

TAKING THE ASE TEST

Make sure you get a good night's sleep the night before the test. Have a good lunch on test day but either eat lightly or skip dinner until after the test. A heavy meal will make you tired.

Bring your admission ticket, some form of photo identification, three or four sharpened #2 pencils and a watch (to keep track of time as the test room may not have a clock) with you to the test center.

The test proctor will explain how to fill out the answer sheet and how much time is allotted for each test. You may take up to four certification tests in one sitting, but this may prove too difficult unless you are very familiar with the subject areas.

When the test begins, open the test booklet to see how many questions are on the test. This will help you keep track of your progress against the time remaining. Mark your answer sheet clearly, making sure the answer number and question number correspond.

Read through each question carefully. If you don't know the answer to a question and need to think about it, move on to the next question. Don't spend too much time on any one question. After you have worked through to the end of the test, check your remaining time and go back and answer the questions you had

Taking An ASE Certification Test

trouble with. Very often, information found in questions later in the test can help answer some of the ones with which you had difficulty.

If you are running out of time and still have unanswered test questions, guess the answers if necessary to make sure every question is answered. Do not leave any answers blank. It is to your advantage to answer every question, because your test score is based on the number of correct answers. A guessed answer could be correct, but a blank answer can never be.

To learn exactly where and when the ASE Certification Tests are available in your area, as well as the costs involved in becoming ASE certified, please contact ASE directly for a registration booklet.

The National Institute for Automotive Service Excellence
101 Blue Seal Drive, S.E.
Suite 101
Leesburg, VA 20175

1-877-ASE-TECH (273-8324)

http://www.ase.com

TABLE OF CONTENTS

Heating And Air Conditioning

TEST SPECIFICATIONS
FOR HEATING AND AIR CONDITIONING (TEST A7)

CONTENT AREA	NUMBER OF QUESTIONS IN ASE TEST	PERCENTAGE OF COVERAGE IN ASE TEST
A. A/C System Service, Diagnosis And Repair	12	24%
B. Refrigeration System Component Diagnosis And Repair	10	20%
1. Compressor And Clutch (5)		
2. Evaporator, Condenser And Related Components (5)		
C. Heating And Engine Cooling Systems Diagnosis And Repair	5	10%
D. Operating Systems And Related Controls Diagnosis And Repair	17	34%
1. Electrical (9)		
2. Vacuum/Mechanical (3)		
3. Automatic And Semi-Automatic Heating, Ventilating And A/C Systems (5)		
E. Refrigerant Recovery, Recycling, Handling And Retrofit	6	12%
Total	**50**	**100%**

The 5-year Recertification Test will cover the same content areas as those listed above. However, the number of questions in each content area of the Recertification Test will be reduced by about one-half.

The following pages list the tasks covered in each content area. These task descriptions offer detailed information to technicians preparing for the test, and to persons who may be instructing Heating and Air Conditioning technicians. The task list may also serve as a guideline for question writers, reviewers and test assemblers.

It should be noted that the number of questions in each content area may not equal the number of tasks listed. Some of the tasks are complex and broad in scope, and may be covered by several questions. Other tasks are simple and narrow in scope; one question may cover several tasks. The main purpose for listing the tasks is to describe accurately what is done on the job, not to make each task correspond to a particular test question.

HEATING AND AIR CONDITIONING TEST TASK LIST

A. A/C SYSTEM SERVICE, DIAGNOSIS AND REPAIR
(12 questions)

Task 1 - Identify system type and conduct performance test on the A/C system; determine needed repairs.

Task 2 - Diagnose A/C system problems indicated by pressure gauge and/or temperature readings; determine needed repairs.

Task 3 - Diagnose A/C system problems indicated by sight, sound, smell and touch procedures; determine needed repairs.

Task 4 - Leak test A/C system; determine needed repairs.

Task 5 - Identify A/C system refrigerant.

Task 6 - Evacuate A/C system.

Task 7 - Inspect A/C system components for contamination.

Task 8 - Charge A/C system with refrigerant (liquid or vapor).

Task 9 - Identify A/C system lubricant type and capacity.

Task 10 - Inspect and replace passenger compartment (cabin air, pollen) filter.

B. REFRIGERATION SYSTEM COMPONENT DIAGNOSIS AND REPAIR
(10 questions)

1. Compressor And Clutch
(5 questions)

Task 1 - Diagnose A/C system problems that cause the protection devices (pressure, thermal and electronic controls) to interrupt system operation; determine needed repairs.

Task 2 - Inspect, test and replace A/C system pressure and thermal protection devices.

Task 3 - Inspect, adjust and replace A/C compressor drive belts, pulleys and tensioners.

Task 4 - Inspect, test, service and replace A/C compressor clutch components or assembly.

Task 5 - Identify required lubricant type; inspect and correct level in A/C compressor.

Task 6 - Inspect, test, service or replace A/C compressor.

Task 7 - Inspect, repair or replace A/C compressor mountings.

2. Evaporator, Condenser And Related Components
(5 questions)

Task 1 - Inspect, repair or replace A/C system mufflers, hoses, lines, filters, fittings and seals.

Task 2 - Inspect A/C condenser for air flow restrictions.

Task 3 - Inspect, test and replace A/C system condenser and mountings.

Task 4 - Inspect and replace receiver/drier or accumulator/drier.

Task 5 - Inspect, test and replace expansion valve(s).

Task 6 - Inspect and replace orifice tube(s).

Task 7 - Inspect, test, clean or replace evaporator(s).

Task 8 - Inspect, clean and repair evaporator housing and water drain.

Task 9 - Inspect, test and replace evaporator pressure/temperature control systems and devices.

Task 10 - Identify, inspect and replace A/C system service valves (gauge connections) and valve caps.

Task 11 - Inspect and replace A/C system high-pressure relief device.

C. HEATING AND ENGINE COOLING SYSTEMS DIAGNOSIS AND REPAIR
(5 questions)

Task 1 - Diagnose the cause of temperature control problems in the heater/ventilation system; determine needed repairs.

Task 2 - Diagnose window fogging problems; determine needed repairs.

Task 3 - Perform engine cooling system tests; determine needed repairs.

Task 4 - Inspect and replace engine cooling and heater system hoses and pipes.

Task 5 - Inspect, test and replace radiator, pressure cap, coolant recovery system and water pump.

Task 6 - Inspect, test and replace thermostat, bypass and housing.

Task 7 - Identify, inspect, recover coolant; flush and refill system with proper coolant.

Task 8 - Inspect, test and replace fan, (both electrical and mechanical), fan clutch, fan belts, fan shroud and air dams.

Task 9 - Inspect, test and replace heater coolant control valve (manual, vacuum and electrical types) and auxiliary coolant pump.

Task 10 - Inspect, flush and replace heater core.

D. OPERATING SYSTEMS AND RELATED CONTROLS DIAGNOSIS AND REPAIR
(17 questions)

1. Electrical
(9 questions)

Task 1 - Diagnose the cause of failures in the electrical control system of heating, ventilating and A/C systems; determine needed repairs.

Task 2 - Inspect, test, repair and replace A/C-heater blower motors, resistors, switches, relay/modules, wiring and protection devices.

Task 3 - Inspect, test, repair and replace A/C compressor clutch coil, relay/modules, wiring, sensors, switches, diodes and protection devices.

Task 4 - Inspect, test, repair, replace and adjust A/C-related engine control systems.

Task 5 - Inspect, test, repair, replace and adjust load sensitive A/C compressor cut-off systems.

Task 6 - Inspect, test, repair and replace engine cooling/condenser fan motors, relays/modules, switches, sensors, wiring and protection devices.

Task 7 - Inspect, test, adjust, repair and replace electric actuator motors, relays/modules, switches, sensors, wiring and protection devices.

Task 8 - Inspect, test, service or replace heating, ventilating and A/C control panel assemblies.

2. Vacuum/Mechanical
(3 questions)

Task 1 - Diagnose the cause of failures in the vacuum and mechanical switches and controls of the heating, ventilating and A/C systems; determine needed repairs.

Task 2 - Inspect, test, service or replace heating, ventilating and A/C control panel assemblies.

Task 3 - Inspect, test, adjust and replace heating, ventilating and A/C control cables and linkages.

Task 4 - Inspect, test and replace heating, ventilating and A/C vacuum actuators (diaphragms/motors) and hoses.

Task 5 - Identify, inspect, test, and replace heating, ventilating and A/C vacuum reservoir, check valve and restrictors.

Task 6 - Inspect, test, adjust, repair or replace heating, ventilating and A/C ducts, doors and outlets.

3. Automatic And Semi-Automatic Heating, Ventilating And A/C Systems
(5 questions)

Task 1 - Diagnose temperature control system problems; determine needed repairs.

Task 2 - Diagnose blower system problems; determine needed repairs.

Task 3 - Diagnose air distribution system problems; determine needed repairs.

Task 4 - Diagnose compressor clutch control system; determine needed repairs.

Task 5 - Inspect, test, adjust or replace climate and blower control sensors.

Task 6 - Inspect, test, adjust and replace door actuator(s).

Task 7 - Inspect, test and replace heater water valve and controls.

Task 8 - Inspect, test and replace electric and vacuum motors, solenoids and switches.

Task 9 - Inspect, test and replace Automatic Temperature Control (ATC) control panel and/or climate control computer (microprocessor/programmer).

Task 10 - Check and adjust calibration of Automatic Temperature Control (ATC) system.

E. REFRIGERANT RECOVERY, RECYCLING, HANDLING AND RETROFIT
(6 questions)

Task 1 - Maintain and verify correct operation of certified equipment.

Task 2 - Identify and recover A/C system refrigerant.

Task 3 - Recycle or properly dispose of refrigerant.

Task 4 - Label and store refrigerant.

Task 5 - Test recycled refrigerant for non-condensable gases.

Task 6 - Follow Federal and local guidelines for retrofit procedures.

The preceding Task List Data details all of the relevant subject matter you are expected to know in order to sit for this ASE Certification Test. Your own years of experience as a professional technician in the automotive service industry should provide you with additional background.

Finally, a conscientious review of the self-study material provided in this Training for ASE Certification unit will help you to be adequately prepared to take this test.

We employ technicians certified by the
National Institute for
**AUTOMOTIVE
SERVICE
EXCELLENCE**
Let us show you their credentials

NOTES

A/C SYSTEM SERVICE, DIAGNOSIS AND REPAIR

A/C SYSTEM OPERATION

In order to understand how an A/C system works, we must first understand a few basic principles. The first, and most important principle is that heat always moves toward a state of less heat. This is how an engine's cooling system works. Heat created by the combustion process in the engine's cylinders is transferred to the coolant in the water jackets next to the cylinders. The coolant is then pumped to the radiator where the heat is transferred to the cooler air traveling through it.

The second principle is that it requires a large amount of heat to change a liquid into a gas. Heat quantity is measured in British Thermal Units (BTUs) and a BTU is the amount of heat that is required to raise the temperature of one pound of water by 1°F. Consider that it takes only 180 BTUs of heat to raise the temperature of one pound of water from 32°F (0°C) to 212°F (100°C), but it requires another 970 BTUs to change that same pound of water into steam at the same temperature. The amount of heat needed for a liquid to change state to a vapor, without the temperature changing, is called the latent heat of evaporation.

The third principle is that when a gas is compressed to a higher pressure, the temperature of the gas is also increased. The best example of this principle is what occurs in the cylinders of a diesel engine. There, the air from the intake is compressed to the point where it becomes so hot that it ignites the fuel as it is

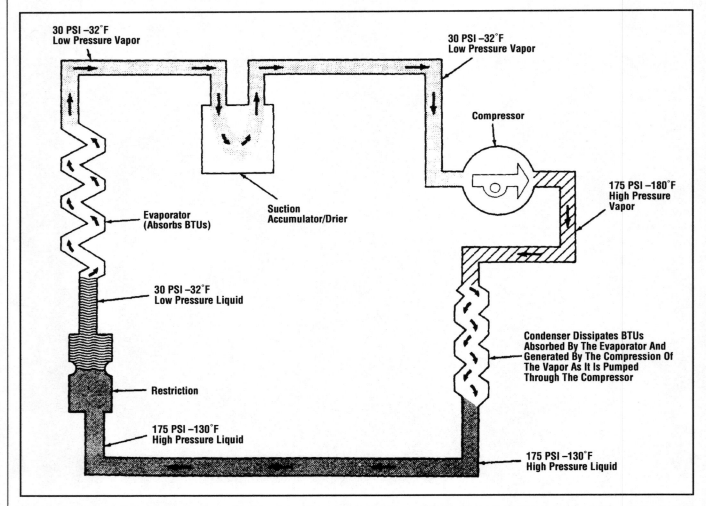

A schematic of the refrigerant cycle. Heat is absorbed as the refrigerant boils in the evaporator and heat is removed as it changes back to a liquid in the condenser. *(Courtesy: Ford Motor Co.)*

injected into the cylinder.

Armed with the knowledge of these principles, let's look at the A/C system. Since hot always moves to cold, to remove heat from inside a vehicle we must put something cold inside the vehicle that can carry the heat away: this is the refrigerant in the evaporator of the A/C system. Refrigerant has a boiling point below 32°F (0°C), which enables it to boil and absorb heat at low temperatures. Liquid refrigerant is metered into the evaporator, where warm air blown through the evaporator by the blower motor causes the liquid refrigerant to boil and change into a vapor, absorbing the latent heat of evaporation.

The refrigerant leaves the evaporator in the form of a gas, however, this gas is still just above 32°F (0°C). Since we know that hot always moves to cold, how can we remove the heat that was absorbed in the evaporator when the ambient air temperature is about 50°F (10°C) warmer? The answer is by compressing the refrigerant gas with the A/C compressor.

As we said earlier, the temper-ature of a gas is raised when it is compressed. In the A/C system, the compressor raises the pressure of the refrigerant gas until its temperature is above ambient. The warmer refrigerant is pumped to the condenser, where relatively cooler ambient air removes the heat, changing the state of the refrigerant back to a liquid. The amount of heat given off as a vapor changes state from a gas to a liquid, without the temperature changing, is called the latent heat of condensation. The liquid refrigerant then leaves the condenser and returns to the refrigerant metering device, where it completes the refrigerant cycle.

Refrigerant is metered into the evaporator by a Thermostatic Expansion Valve (TXV) or an orifice tube, depending on the type of system. If the system is equipped with a TXV, liquid refrigerant will pass through a receiver/drier after it leaves the condenser and before it enters the TXV. If the system uses an orifice tube, the refrigerant flows through an accumulator before it enters the compressor.

Both the TXV and the orifice tube create a restriction in the system against which the compressor forces the refrigerant. Before the refrigerant passes through the TXV or orifice tube, it is under high pressure. Beyond that point the refrigerant is under low pressure. In fact, it is common to refer to the high side and low side of the A/C system when discussing function and problems. Everything between the compressor and the TXV (or orifice tube) is on the high side; everything from the TXV (or orifice tube) back to the compressor is on the low side.

The specifications for the high pressures and low pressures vary from vehicle to vehicle, system to system, manufacturer to manufacturer, and also according to whether R12 or R134a refrigerant is being used. These pressures must be kept in balance in order for the A/C system to function properly. Or, to put it more accurately, we must prevent the evaporator or condenser from becoming too cold or too warm. The TXV and orifice tube act as system control devices, but these components by themselves do not control the refrigerant flow accu-

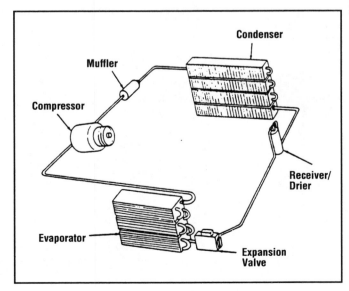

A typical expansion valve equipped air conditioning system.

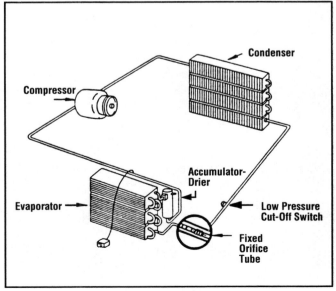

A typical orifice tube equipped air conditioning system.

rately enough to maintain precise evaporator temperature. Over the years, various methods have been employed to achieve this, but today, there are two that are most common:

• Applying or removing electricity to the compressor electromagnetic clutch, having it engage and disengage

• By changing the actual operating displacement of the compressor.

Clutch Cycling Systems

Cycling the clutch is a simple way to control the system and is actually the most common method currently in use. Cycling clutch control works with both the TXV and orifice tube systems, but because orifice tubes don't open and close like expansion valves, they will always be found working in conjunction with cycling clutch control.

The amount of heat that the evaporator must remove affects the system pressure. Since R12 and R134a have roughly a one-to-one relationship between pressure and temperature (for each degree the refrigerant warms, the pressure goes up one psi), if we control the pressure within the evaporator, we also control its temperature. The compressor cycling rate automatically changes to control the temperature. The clutch is turned off and on by a switch to prevent the evaporator from icing. During operation, the clutch may be cycled several times each minute. As the change in heat load on the evaporator affects system pressures, the compressor cycling rate automatically changes to achieve the desired temperature.

Many orifice tube systems use some type of pressure cycling switch. It senses the low side pressure (which is directly proportionate to temperature). Often, the pressure cycling switch is mounted on the accu-mulator. Since system pressure is quite low during cold weather, the pressure cycling switch keeps the compressor from running when it isn't needed. It also protects the compressor from damage should the refrigerant charge escape, since the compressor is lubricated by oil flowing with refrigerant.

A typical TXV system has a bulb and/or capillary tube or some other type of temperature sensing device embedded in the evaporator fins or attached to the evaporator outlet pipe. This device works in conjunction with a switch. When evaporator temperature increases, the switch closes and the compressor clutch engages. When evaporator temperature decreases, the switch opens and the clutch disengages.

For both orifice tube and expansion valve systems, the temperatures (and therefore pressures) at which the compressor clutch is cycled vary by system, vehicle and refrigerant.

Variable Displacement Compressors

Variable displacement compressors look and operate like conventional compressors, but operate differently. These can be used in systems equipped with either an expansion valve or orifice tube, but even when used in an orifice tube system, the clutch does not cycle. These systems control refrigerant flow by actually changing the operating displacement of the compressor. When cooling demand is high, the compressor will operate at full displacement, moving a large volume of refrigerant through the system. When cooling demand is lower, the compressor can operate at displacements from just about full, all the way down to just about none. Variable displacement compressors can be either a vane type or piston design. Piston design is the most common, but all variable displacement compressors essentially use the same method of operation.

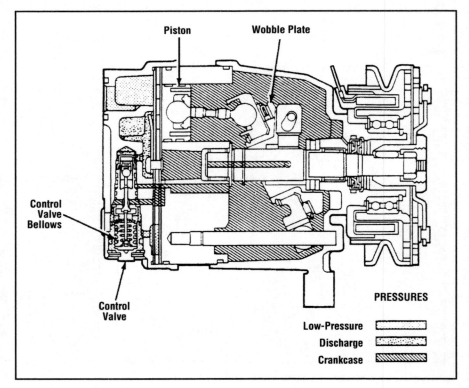

A typical piston type variable displacement compressor.

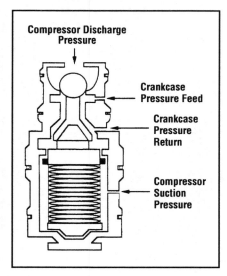

A control valve as installed in a variable displacement compressor.

Variable displacement compressors are of a wobble plate design. The wobble plate moves the pistons up and down in their bores as the compressor shaft rotates. The angle of the wobble plate changes to control piston stroke. A control valve mounted directly in the compressor senses relative pressures at both ends of the pistons within the compressor crankcase. Wobble plate angle changes are controlled by changes in crankcase pressure. When cooling demand is high, the control valve bleeds pressure into the compressor's suction cavity, keeping crankcase pressure low. The angle of the wobble plate becomes severe, maintaining maximum stroke and displacement, and therefore maximum refrigerant flow. When cooling demand is lower, crankcase pressure is kept higher by the control valve opening a passage between the discharge port and the crankcase. Now, the angle of the wobble plate becomes less severe, reducing displacement and refrigerant flow. How severe the angle of the wobble plate becomes to determine displacement and flow, depends on cooling demand at any given time.

One big advantage of variable displacement compressors is their smooth operation, since the clutch does not cycle on-and-off. This has a very positive effect on engine idle quality and passenger comfort.

Additional A/C System Benefits

In addition to removing heat from the passenger compartment of the vehicle, the A/C system also removes moisture (humidity) from the air inside the vehicle as well as some airborne dust and pollen. Some vehicles are even equipped with dust and pollen filters.

The hot air inside the vehicle contains an elevated level of humidity. As it passes over the surface of the cooler evaporator, moisture is removed as it condenses and collects on the evaporator. This moisture collected on the surface of the evaporator then drips out of the evaporator case onto the ground. The airborne dust and pollen become trapped in the water droplets collected on the evaporator, and then drip out onto the ground with the moisture.

A/C SYSTEM PERFORMANCE TESTING

System Identification

Before testing system performance, the type of refrigerant used and the design method used to regulate system pressures and temperatures must be identified. Systems that use R134a refrigerant usually have identification labels on various system components. On R12 systems, the service port fittings are a male screw on type, and when sized differently, the high side port is smaller in diameter. R134a systems use quick connect fittings, similar to the ones used on air tools, and this time the low side port is the smaller one.

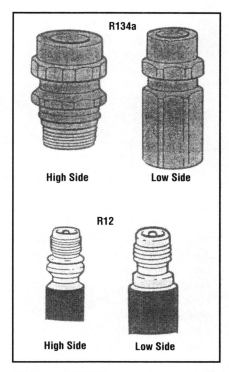

R12 and R134a service port fittings.

As stated earlier, A/C systems can be identified by whether an expansion valve or orifice tube is used to control refrigerant flow into the evaporator and by whether the compressor cycles on and off or runs continuously. Systems using an expansion valve have a receiver/drier between the valve and condenser, while orifice tube systems have an accumulator between the evaporator and compressor. Continuously running compressors use a suction throttling device to control evaporator pressure and temperature. This can be a Suction Throttling Valve (SVT) or Pilot Operated Absolute (POA) valve, either of which would be located at the evaporator outlet, or an Evaporator Pressure Regulator (EPR) located on the compressor.

Some systems use **components** that combine the **functions** of components that are **usually** separate on other systems. A Valves In Receiver (VIR) assembly incorporates the expansion valve, POA valve and receiver/drier functions in one unit. The VIR is located next to the evaporator, where it is connected **to** both the inlet and outlet lines.

Refrigerants

The refrigerant **used** in automotive air conditioning systems from their inception until the early 1990s was a **substance** most popularly known as Freon® or R12, which is a **chlorinated** fluorocarbon (CFC). Although it works extremely well as a heat transfer medium in **an** automotive air conditioning system, it has been found to **have** a devastating effect on the **earth's** ozone layer, which protects **all** life on earth from harmful **ultraviolet** radiation from the **sun**. When a chlorine atom from **a** CFC like R12 is released, it **can** rise into the stratosphere **and** combine with one of the oxygen atoms of an ozone molecule **to form** chlorine monoxide and **an** oxygen molecule, destroying **that** ozone molecule. Since **R12** was very inexpensive, it **was** a common practice to release **it** into the atmosphere during **the** servicing of an air conditioning **system**.

The Clean Air Act of 1990 required that the **automotive** industry stop releasing ozone damaging refrigerant into the atmosphere. All **refrigerants** must now be recovered when performing system **service** and R12 refrigerant has **been** replaced with R134a or HFC134a, which is not harmful to the **ozone** layer. However, R134a is **still** classified as a global **warming** gas, and alternative **refrigerants** like R152a and R744, **which** do not contribute as **much** to global

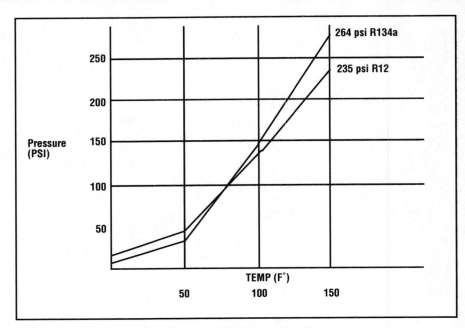

Refrigerant Temperature/Pressure Relationship Chart.

warming, are being considered for future use. In this study guide, we will confine our discussion to R12 and R134a, the two types of refrigerant currently used.

R12 and R134a are gasses at room temperature. In fact, R12 doesn't turn to a liquid until it reaches about –22°F (–30°C) and R134a doesn't turn to a liquid until it reaches about –15°F (–26°C). These refrigerants also possess another unique feature: they both have roughly a one to one temperature to pressure relationship. This means that for every one psi increase in pressure, the boiling point increases one degree. Due to this relationship, by controlling pressure, we can control evaporation or boiling.

R12 and R134a cannot be mixed. Even though they operate very similarly, they are distinctly different chemicals, and they require different approaches to certain system components, materials, and lubricating oils. A mixture of these two refrigerants can result in higher than normal pressures within a system or

refrigerant container.

According to the EPA, when a vehicle is retrofitted from R12 to any other type of refrigerant, a label identifying the new refrigerant in the system must be placed in plain view in the engine compartment, and new fittings that are unique to that refrigerant must be attached to the service ports of the A/C system. Obviously, these requirements don't solve the entire identification problem, and you could find a vehicle that has been retrofitted but has not been labeled, or a vehicle that has the right label, but has contaminated refrigerant.

This is where a refrigerant identifier unit can help pinpoint problems. Depending on the manufacturer, the identifier can be a hand-held tool, which will identify whether the refrigerant is pure R12 or R134a, or be part of a complete refrigerant recovery/recycling station, which can aid in complete A/C diagnostics. Always follow the identifier manufacturer's instructions when using this type of equipment.

Also be aware that mixing different types of refrigerant can result in a mixture that is not recognized by the identifier because the original intent was to identify R12 and R134a refrigerants.

Preliminary Inspection

Visually inspect the A/C system for obvious problems. Check the compressor drive belt for evidence of cracking, fraying, glazing or other damage and replace as necessary. If the belt is adjustable, check the belt tension by pressing against the belt with moderate pressure at a point midway along the longest span, and compare the deflection with specification, or check the tension using a belt tension gauge. Make sure the compressor is attached securely to its mounting brackets and the mounting bushings are in good condition.

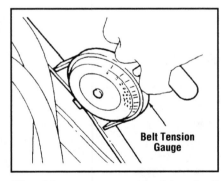

Belt Tension Gauge

Checking compressor drive belt tension using a belt tension gauge. (Courtesy: Ford Motor Co.)

Check the refrigerant lines and hoses for damage and signs of oil leakage, especially at any connections or unions. If oil has leaked out, most likely the refrigerant has as well. Pay particular attention to connections that are subject to engine vibrations, usually those on rubber lines. Check the front of the compressor. Oil here often indicates a bad front seal. Check all fittings and the pressure relief valve for signs of leaks.

Inspect the system electrical wiring to the compressor, blower motor and A/C switches for any damage. Make sure all connections are clean and tight. Check the vacuum hoses between the engine and firewall for evidence of cracks, splits, kinks or other damage that could cause a vacuum leak.

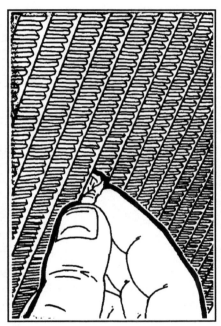

The position of the condenser in front of the radiator makes it particularly susceptible to collecting debris.

Inspect the condenser for debris that may block air flow. If too many fins are bent, air flow will be reduced. Inspect the fan shroud for broken or missing parts, and make sure all air dams and condenser side and air seals are in place as they should be. Also, check the fresh air intakes in the cowl for leaves and other such debris.

If equipped with a mechanical fan, check the drive belt for wear and belt tension. A slipping belt will cause the fan to turn too slowly and not draw enough air through the condenser. Check the back of the fan clutch for an oily film, which would indicate that fluid is leaking and replacement is necessary. Turn the fan and clutch assembly by hand; there should be some viscous drag, but it should turn smoothly during a full rotation. Replace the fan clutch if it does not turn smoothly or if it does not turn at all. It should also be replaced if there is no viscous drag when hot or cold.

Manifold Gauges

A manifold gauge set is used to read the pressures on the low side and high side of the system. The gauge set has a low pressure gauge and a high pressure gauge. The gauges and hoses are often color coded blue for low, red for high. The low side is connected to the service fitting that is located somewhere between the evaporator outlet and the compressor. The high side fitting is located somewhere between the compressor and the expansion valve or orifice tube.

A center hose or hoses, usually yellow in color, and often referred to as the service hose, connects to a vacuum pump or refrigerant source for evacuating or charging the system. All hoses must have a shutoff within 12-in. of their ends to prevent excess refrigerant from escaping during connection and disconnection. A Schrader valve or quick disconnect device at the hose end fitting is most common.

WARNING: Always wear eye and skin protection when working with refrigerant, or personal injury may result.

To connect the gauge set, first locate the service fittings. Make sure the valves on the manifold and hoses are closed. Remove the cap from the low side service fitting and connect the low side

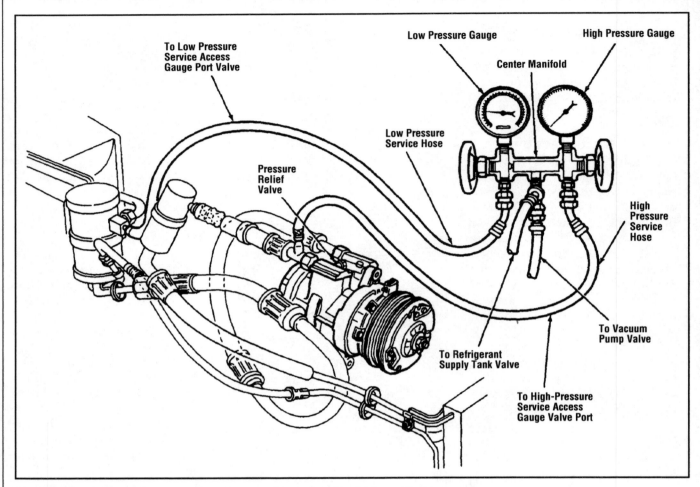

Typical manifold gauge set connections. *(Courtesy: Ford Motor Co.)*

hose to the fitting. Remove the high side service fitting cap. Some high side service ports require that an adapter be fitted to connect the high side hose. If necessary, install the adapter and connect the hose to the adapter or fitting.

Open each hose valve but leave the manifold valves closed. The system pressure can now be read on the gauges.

Performance Testing

A performance test can determine whether the A/C system is functioning properly and if it is not can indicate what is wrong so the system can be repaired. Different vehicle manufacturers specify different methods to conduct system performance checks,

but as a guideline, the following procedure may be used.

Connect a manifold gauge set as previously described. Hang the gauge set or place it where the gauges can be seen, making sure the hoses will not contact any hot or moving engine parts. With the engine off, the high and low side pressures should be equal and the pressure should be correct for the ambient temperature. For example, at 70°F (21°C), the pressure in a system with R12 refrigerant should be about 70 psi, while a system with R134a should be slightly higher at 71 psi.

Place a thermometer at the center dash panel duct outlet to indicate the system temperature and place another thermometer at the center of the grille to regis-

ter ambient temperature. Start the engine and turn on the A/C. Set the temperature control to the coldest setting. Turn on the blower motor and make sure it works on all speeds. Generally, if one of the blower speeds doesn't work, the problem is a faulty resistor. If the high speed doesn't work, the problem could be the high speed relay or fuse. If the blower is too slow at all speeds, perform a current draw test to see if the windings or brushes are bad.

At this point, if the A/C system is operating properly, there should be cool to cold air coming from the instrument panel air ducts. When the temperature control is moved from the coolest to the warmest setting, the air temperature should change to warm. When the function control lever is moved from A/C to heat, the air flow should move to the floor ducts.

Place the function control in the 'MAX A/C' or 'RECIRC' position and set the temperature control to the coldest position. Close all of the vehicle's doors and windows and make sure that all dash panel duct outlets are open.

Run the system on high for about five minutes, and then reduce the blower speed to low and allow the system to stabilize for about five more minutes. The thermometer at the center dash panel duct should read 35°- 55°F (2° - 13°C), depending on ambient temperature and humidity.

NOTE: *Some vehicle manufacturers may recommend that you place a large fan in front of the grille to provide sufficient air flow over the condenser while performing this test.*

Check the vehicle manufacturer's specifications for proper system operating pressures, especially on R134a systems. Normal high side gauge readings depend on the ambient temperature, so it is best to consult a temperature/pressure chart. Normal low side readings vary depending on what is happening in the system, particularly in the evaporator, and what type of system it is. The system controls (clutch cycling, expansion valve opening and closing, etc.) affect the readings and affect the evaporator temperature since there is roughly a one-to-one-relationship between temperature and pressure. Always look up the specifications for the system being worked on.

Here are some examples of gauge readings and what they may indicate:

Low side normal, high side normal (but poor cooling)
• air or moisture in the system
• blend door stuck open (admitting too much heat)

• defective or misadjusted thermostatic switch
• defective pressure cycling switch.

Low side low, high side low
• low refrigerant charge (possible leak)
• expansion valve stuck closed
• restriction on the high side.

Low side high, high side high
• damaged compressor (bent or damaged valves)
• refrigerant overcharge
• condenser restriction or inoperative fan
• expansion valve stuck open.

Low side high, high side low
• damaged compressor (bent or damaged valves)
• loose drive belt or slipping clutch (if there's no compressor noise).

Low side low, high side normal to high
• expansion valve stuck closed

Ambient Air Temperature	Relative Humidity	Service Port Pressure		Maximum Left Center Discharge Air Temperature
		Low Side	High Side	
13–16°C (55–65°F)	0–100%	175–206 kPa (25–30 psi)	340–850 kPa (49–123 psi)	7°C (45°F)
19–24°C (66–75°F)	Below 40%	175–215 kPa (25–31 psi)	430–930 kPa (62–135 psi)	6°C (43°F)
	Above 40%	175–254 kPa (25–37 psi)	570–1070 kPa (83–155 psi)	9°C (48°F)
25–29°C (76–85°F)	Below 35%	175–249 kPa (25–36 psi)	760–1410 kPa (147–205 psi)	9°C (42°F)
	35–60%	175–261 kPa (26–38 psi)	830–1180 kPa (120–171 psi)	10°C (50°F)
	Above 60%	185–286 kPa (27–42 psi)	880–1250 kPa (128–181 psi)	11°C (52°F)
30–35°C (86–95°F)	Below 30%	193–293 kPa (28–43 psi)	1010–1410 kPa (146–205 psi)	12°C (54°F)
	30–50%	228–269 kPa (30–44 psi)	1050–1440 kPa (153–209 psi)	13°C (55°F)
	Above 50%	221–324 kPa (32–47 psi)	1100–1470 kPa (160–213 psi)	14°C (58°F)
36–41°C (96–105°F)	Below 20%	241–337 kPa (35–47 psi)	1310–1700 kPa (190–246 psi)	16°C (61°F)
	20–40%	247–345 kPa (36–50 psi)	1320–1700 kPa (190–230 psi)	16°C (61°F)
	Above 40%	259–353 kPa (37–52 psi)	1350–1690 kPa (196–246 psi)	16°C (61°F)
42–46°C (106–115°F)	Below 20%	292–378 kPa (42–55 psi)	1630–1950 kPa (238–283 psi)	17°C (62°F)
	Above 20%	297–383 kPa (43–55 psi)	1620–1930 kPa (235–280 psi)	19°C (66°F)
47–49°C (116–120°F)	Below 30%	338–405 kPa (50–59 psi)	187–2080 kPa (271–302 psi)	20°C (68°F)

A typical A/C performance specifications chart for an R134a vehicle. It shows how ambient temperature and relative humidity affect system operating pressures and outlet temperatures. *(Courtesy: GM Corp.)*

- clogged orifice tube.

Common causes of high pressure:
- refrigerant overcharge
- restricted condenser (leaves, paper, bugs, etc.)
- clogged receiver/drier
- plugged orifice tube.

DIAGNOSIS BY SIGHT, SOUND, SMELL AND TOUCH

Sight

If the system has a sight glass, observe the refrigerant as it passes by. If it is clear, the charge is correct. If there is foam, the charge is low, but if there are only a couple of bubbles, it is probably OK. A few bubbles when the compressor cycles on is normal. Oil streaks in the sight glass usually indicate a low charge and that the compressor is pumping oil from its sump. If the sight glass is cloudy, the desiccant bag has probably burst. Systems with orifice tubes and accumulators usually don't have sight glasses. Also, if an R134a system has a sight glass, do not use it to try to perform diagnosis, as it is normal to observe bubbles in this type of system. If the refrigerant is red, someone has probably added refrigerant with a leak detection dye; this is no reason for concern.

Look for frost buildup on the A/C lines and components. If there is a restriction in the system, frost will accumulate at the point of the restriction. A restricted receiver/drier will have frost buildup. A flooded evaporator, which can be caused by a restricted TXV, will have frost buildup at the evaporator outlet. Keep in mind that it is normal for light frost buildup at the outlet of the refrigerant metering device.

Sound

Squealing sounds are perhaps the most common noises. Usually,

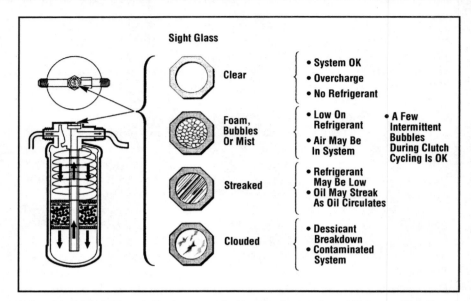

What is visible in the sight glass can help with diagnosing system malfunctions.

the belts are the culprits. Sometimes belt noise sounds a lot like bearing noise. Spray some water on the belts and see if the noise goes away. If it does, the tension may need to be corrected or the belts may have to be replaced.

Bad compressor or clutch bearings may also make noise. Start the engine and engage the compressor clutch. Defective compressor bearings won't make noise until the compressor is operating, but bad clutch bearings will most often make noise without the clutch engaged. To verify defective pulley bearings, remove the belt(s) and turn the pulley by hand. If there is roughness, the bearings are bad. If there is no roughness, the compressor shaft bearing or thrust bearing may be the cause. Make sure you observe the proper clutch air gap specification if you need to replace a clutch or field coil assembly.

A clicking or buzzing noise coming from the compressor is a sign that the system is overcharged and liquid refrigerant is entering the compressor. Unless some refrigerant is removed,

severe compressor damage may result. This noise could also result from air in the system. Knocking sounds usually indicate internal compressor damage, especially on piston type compressors. Knocking sounds can also be the result of loose compressor mounting bolts.

Noises from the blower motor could point to a bad bearing or debris, such as leaves, in the blower plenum.

Smell

Foul odors caused by bacterial growth can originate from the evaporator and evaporator case. As explained earlier, the evaporator removes moisture from the air as it condenses and collects on the cool evaporator surface. The moisture then drips from the evaporator and drains from a tube in the bottom of the evaporator case.

If the drain at the bottom of the evaporator case becomes clogged and water collects and stagnates, or if the surface of the evaporator remains too moist due to high humidity, bacteria can grow in the stagnant water or on the evaporator surface and cause an odor. This odor is then sent into the passenger compartment by the blower motor.

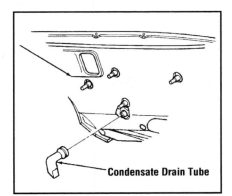

Typical evaporator case drain tube. *(Courtesy: DaimlerChrysler Corp.)*

To prevent stagnant water from collecting, make sure the evaporator case drain is clear. In some instances a clogged drain can cause the evaporator case to fill up and leak water into the passenger compartment. To prevent bacterial growth on the evaporator surface, the system should be run periodically on vent or heat with the A/C off, to dry the evaporator. Chemical fungicides can be used to kill the bacteria. Depending on the vehicle, the evaporator and/or case may have to be removed or the evaporator fins may be able to be accessed by removing the blower motor resistor.

Touch

Feel the temperature of the A/C lines and hoses during A/C operation. It is normal for the high side components to be warm or hot and the low side components to be cool or cold. If you feel along the high side components and suddenly the surface turns cold, you have discovered a restriction in the system at the point of temperature change. On humid days, frost may even form at this point. If frost forms at the evaporator outlet, it could be

caused by a defective Pilot Operated Absolute (POA) valve, Suction Throttling Valve (STV) or thermostatic switch. If frost forms on the outside of the TXV, it may be stuck closed or clogged with ice.

A receiver/drier should be warm and an accumulator should be cool. The evaporator outlet should be cool; if it is not, the system may be low on refrigerant or the proper amount of refrigerant may not be entering the evaporator. The line from the condenser to the TXV or orifice tube should be warm to hot. Feel the compressor itself. It may be warm, but if it is very hot, the valves may be broken or bent. This is particularly true of a piston-type compressor if the head is hot.

REFRIGERANT LEAK DETECTION

NOTE: The most common leak detector used to be a propane bottle with a special head, but their use is no longer recommended for a few reasons. First, they cannot detect leakage of R134a. Second, they are not sensitive enough to detect very small leaks, as is now required. Third, R12 drawn into a flame can produce a poisonous gas.

As stated earlier, the presence of oil residue at a line connection is usually the sign of a refrigerant leak, because the refrigerant oil will escape along with the refrigerant. Visually inspect all line and hose connections, the area around the compressor seal, the service port fittings and the condenser and evaporator.

A solution of soap and water is the simplest and cheapest leak detector. Simply apply the soapy

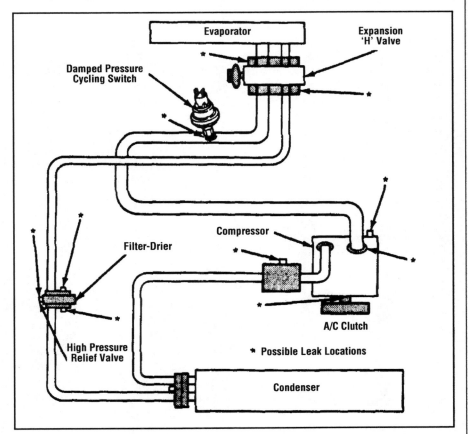

This schematic indicates areas where refrigerant leaks are most likely to occur. *(Courtesy: DaimlerChrysler Corp.)*

water to the suspected area with a brush or spray bottle and look for the presence of bubbles or foam, which would be caused by a leak. The problem with this method is that it is only useful for a large leak.

Electronic leak detectors and fluorescent dye detectors are the preferred methods for finding refrigerant leaks.

Electronic Leak Detectors

Electronic leak detectors signal the presence of refrigerant by some type of audible indication, usually a beeping, clicking or buzzing tone. The more rapid the beeps, or the louder the tone, the larger the leak. These detectors usually have a sensitivity adjustment: in maximum position, they will detect leaks as small as one half ounce of refrigerant a year. To find leaks, at least 50 psi must be in the system. To be sure that the system is under pressure, connect the gauge set. If the pressure is below 50 lbs., add refrigerant to get enough pressure for testing.

Perform the leak check in a location that is free of wind and drafts. If the area is contaminated

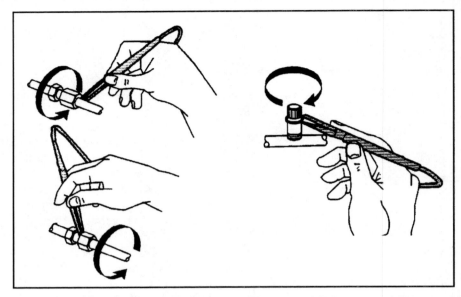

Move the leak detector probe all the away around fitting connections and service port fittings. Don't move the probe any faster than around one inch per second. *(Courtesy: GM Corp.)*

with refrigerant, use a fan to blow the excess refrigerant away. Make sure that you pass the probe around the bottom of components and hoses as refrigerant is heavier than air and tends to settle. Don't move the probe too quickly, as this may cause you to miss small leaks. No faster than one inch per second is the general rule. Concentrate your efforts at connections and fittings as these are the most likely leak sites. And last but not least, if you intend to use an electronic leak detector on an R134a system, make sure it is designed for such, as many older units are not.

Leak Detection With Fluorescent Dye

Another way to find leaks is by injecting a special fluorescent dye into the system, operating it for a short time, and then passing an ultraviolet light over all of the components. This is a good method to find very small leaks, or leaks in inconvenient places. There is a difference between the dyes to be used in R12 and R134a systems, so be sure to use

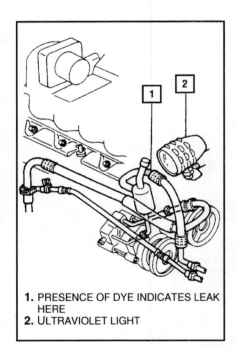

1. PRESENCE OF DYE INDICATES LEAK HERE
2. ULTRAVIOLET LIGHT

Using an ultraviolet light to detect dye and refrigerant leaks. *(Courtesy: Ford Motor Co.)*

the proper type for the system being worked on.

REFRIGERANT RECOVERY

Unless the refrigerant has

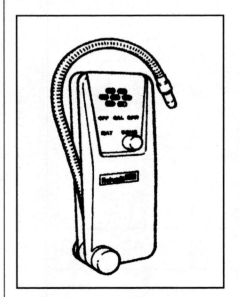

Typical electronic leak detector. *(Courtesy: Ford Motor Co.)*

completely drained from the A/C system due to a leak, before replacing any components that carry refrigerant through the system, the refrigerant must be removed. On a typical 80°F (27°C) day, a fully charged system will have over 80 psi of pressure. Opening a fitting or union will allow the refrigerant to escape into the atmosphere. Such a procedure is not only unsafe, it is illegal and environmentally harmful.

equipment is operated in accordance with the manufacturer's instructions.

SYSTEM EVACUATION

After repairs have been performed on the A/C system, or any time the system has been opened, it must be evacuated. When repairs are made, air will enter the open system, and if not removed, the air can cause higher than normal operating pressures, leading to poor cooling

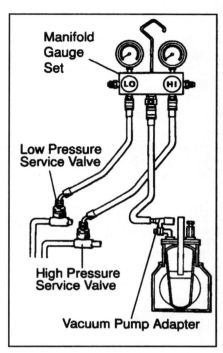

Evacuating the A/C system using a stand-alone vacuum pump. *(Courtesy: Toyota Motor Corp.)*

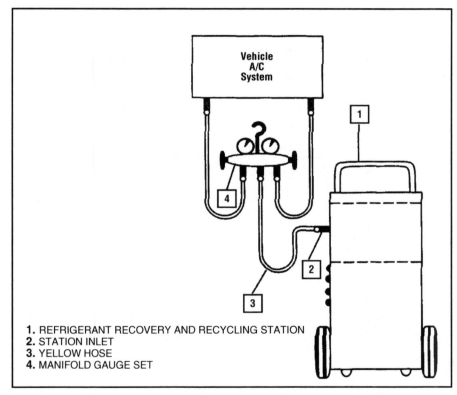

1. REFRIGERANT RECOVERY AND RECYCLING STATION
2. STATION INLET
3. YELLOW HOSE
4. MANIFOLD GAUGE SET

Recovering refrigerant from the A/C system. *(Courtesy: GM Corp.)*

All refrigerant must be extracted and recycled using approved recovery/recycling equipment. Most units operate similarly. The service hoses are properly connected to the vehicle's A/C system, and the equipment is activated to draw out the refrigerant. Once the refrigerant is safely stored, repairs to the A/C system can be performed. Make sure the recovery/recycling

performance.

Moisture from humidity in the air can form destructive chemicals inside the system when mixed with refrigerant and oils, and can cause a breakdown of the newer synthetic oils used in R134a systems. Also, water in the system can ice up in the expansion valve and block refrigerant flow. On systems with R12, water can combine with the chlorine in

the R12 to form hydrochloric acid. These chemicals can corrode metals and attack rubber parts. During evacuation, as the pressure inside the system lowers, so does the boiling point of the water in the system. At 29-in. Hg, water can vaporize and be withdrawn by the vacuum pump.

While stand-alone vacuum pumps are commercially available, if you are using a charging station, the vacuum pump is most likely incorporated into the station. After properly connecting the service hoses, start the vacuum pump and open both sides of the system, exposing it to vacuum. Once the vacuum level reaches specification, continue pulling the vacuum for at least 30 to 60 minutes. The more humid the air, the longer the vacuum pump should be allowed to run. If the pump is turned off too soon, some of the moisture in the system will be left behind. Close all valves and turn the pump off.

Wait for 5 minutes and note any vacuum loss. Loss of vacuum within 5 minutes indicates leakage. Before turning off the pump, close off the A/C system to the atmosphere to prevent air from being drawn back into it.

Although evacuating removes moisture, it won't remove the oil, nor will it remove debris. To clean out the system, filters can be installed, usually in the liquid line. These filters are usually capable of trapping all debris normally encountered in any system while allowing the refrigerant to pass freely. A system may also be flushed with a special machine to remove debris, but not all system manufacturers recommend this procedure.

REFRIGERANT CHARGING

Although charging the system can be performed through either the high side or low side when the engine is not running, it must be done only through the low side when the engine is running. This safety measure prevents high side pressure from entering the refrigerant container and possibly causing an explosion.

Obtain the refrigerant capacity specification for the system before charging. This is often printed on a sticker located somewhere under the hood, or in a service manual. The most accurate method to assure that the proper amount of refrigerant has been installed into the system is to use some type of charging station that can be programmed to deliver the exact amount. It is crucial that the exact amount of refrigerant called for is used. Overcharging can cause system damage, and undercharging will cause poor performance. With reduced system capacities, especially in R134a systems, charge amounts are more critical than ever. When using a charging station or recovery/recycling equipment, follow the manufacturer's instructions for its use. Allow the system to stabilize for a short period of time after charging. Then performance check the system, noting proper operating gauge pressures.

REFRIGERANT OIL

The main purpose of refrigerant oil is to provide compressor lubrication. The oil travels with the refrigerant throughout the entire system, and in fact relies on the refrigerant to carry it around. The oil has a secondary purpose—to lubricate seals and O-rings and keep them pliable, and also to keep expansion valves moving freely.

Refrigerant oils are designed specifically for air conditioning systems and other types of oils must not be substituted. All R12 systems generally use mineral oil. R134a systems can use two different types of synthetic oils, Polyalkyline Glycol, or PAG for short, or Polyol Ester, most often referred to as just ester. Most R134a vehicles come equipped with PAG, but a few manufacturers use ester.

Mineral oil cannot be used with R134a, and synthetic oils must not be used with R12. The reason for this is that mineral oil does not mix with R134a, and therefore will not travel through the system with the refrigerant; it will just collect in various locations within the system and not provide the needed lubrication for the compressor and other components.

Checking And Adding Oil

Although many older compressors had oil sumps, most newer ones do not. On sumpless systems, the best procedure is to measure the amount of oil found in the component being removed, and then to add that amount of oil back to the system prior to recharging. Although it is always

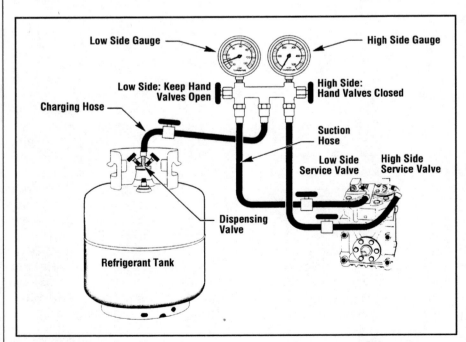

Although a charging station is more accurate, an A/C system can be charged from a refrigerant drum. The drum should be placed on a scale and the total weight noted before charging. During charging, the scale should be watched to determine the amount of refrigerant used.

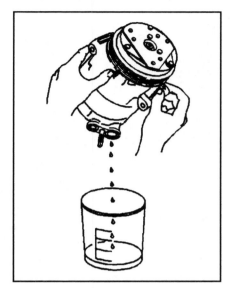

When replacing a compressor, drain the oil from the compressor being removed into a graduated container. Record the amount of refrigerant oil drained from the compressor and then properly dispose of the used oil. Drain any oil from the new compressor. Add the recorded amount of new refrigerant oil to the compressor prior to installation.

best to follow the manufacturer's specific capacities, the following capacities may be used as a rule of thumb when replacing the component:
- condenser-1 oz.
- evaporator-3 oz.
- receiver/drier-1 oz.
- accumulator-2 to 3 oz.
- compressor-amount drained from old unit.

Use only fresh, untainted, moisture free refrigeration oil and recap the bottle immediately. If the cap is left off, even for a short time, the oil will absorb moisture from the air. Always add the oil directly to the compressor if it is the item being replaced. For other components, it doesn't matter where the oil is added.

PASSENGER COMPARTMENT AIR FILTER

Many newer vehicles are equipped with passenger compartment air filters to trap dust and pollen. These filters are usually located at the air intake. The filter should be replaced at the intervals specified in the manufacturer's scheduled maintenance information.

On some vehicles the filter is located under the cowl screen and accessed from outside the vehicle, while on others it is installed in the evaporator case and is accessed from under the dash. Refer to the vehicle service manual for specific procedures.

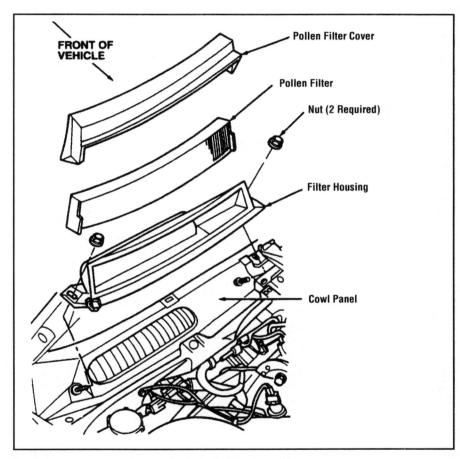

Typical passenger compartment air filter installation. *(Courtesy: Ford Motor Co.)*

NOTES

REFRIGERATION SYSTEM COMPONENT DIAGNOSIS AND REPAIR

COMPRESSOR AND CLUTCH

There are several different compressor designs, but all perform the same function: they move, or pump the refrigerant throughout the system, and they compress the low pressure vaporized refrigerant into a high pressure vapor.

Compressors may be of a piston, rotary vane, or scroll design. Piston style compressors are the most popular, and are either in line, V-type, radial, axial, or wobble plate. The most modern compressors are of a multi-piston design, ranging anywhere from 4 to 10 cylinders. Some compressors change displacement while operating, and have an effect on refrigerant flow in the system.

One thing all modern compressors have in common is a clutch and drive pulley. The pulley is belt-driven by one or two V-belts directly from the engine's crankshaft or by a multi-ribbed V-belt or serpentine belt. The pulley turns whenever the engine is running, although the compressor clutch is not engaged when the air conditioning is turned off.

Compressor Protection Devices

High-Pressure Cutout Switch

When certain malfunctions occur, high side pressures could exceed the safe operating limits of the compressor, hoses or other components. To prevent this from happening, many systems are equipped with high-pressure cutout switches. These switches open the clutch circuit in the event that pressures become excessive. This function shuts down the compressor and stops the pressure from climbing higher. This serves two purposes: it protects the compressor from damage, and prevents venting of refrigerant through the pressure relief device (if equipped). Once repairs are made, the switch will allow normal clutch engagement. Many R12 systems and virtually all R134a systems are equipped with high-pressure cutout switches.

High-pressure conditions can indicate failures such as a damaged compressor, refrigerant overcharge, condenser restriction, stuck open expansion valve, clogged orifice tube or receiver/drier.

Low-Pressure Cutout Switch

Some vehicles are equipped with low-pressure cutout switches. The purpose of this switch is also compressor protection. The compressor clutch circuit is opened if the pressure in the system drops too low. This would be an indication that the system has lost some or all of its refrigerant charge. Since the lubricating oil is carried by the refrigerant, a loss could cause damage to the compressor if it were allowed to operate without sufficient lubrication.

Low-pressure conditions can indicate failures such as a clogged orifice tube, low refrigerant charge, expansion valve stuck closed, or a restriction in the high side of the A/C system.

Ambient Temperature Switch

In non-automatic temperature control systems (ATC), the function of the ambient temperature switch is to inhibit compressor clutch operation in cold ambient temperatures. This sensor opens the electrical path to the compressor clutch when the temperature is below a specified range. This function mainly protects the compressor from poor or no lubrication, which could be the result of cold refrigerant oil.

Electronic Compressor Controls

Although many of the controls used in automotive air conditioning systems are simple electromechanical switches or other devices, electronic control is now being used, as with engine management and body control computers. Compressor clutch engagement can be determined by the computer when conditions like engine coolant temperature, ambient temperature, throttle position, engine load, etc. are optimum for proper system operation. Sensors report on these conditions to the electronic control module (ECM), and the ECM processes this information. If conditions are right, the ECM sends a command to engage the compressor clutch. Conversely, when a problem is detected where conditions are not optimum, the compressor is disengaged by the ECM. Some of the most common sensors that computers use to help them make clutch operation decisions are:

Engine Coolant And Ambient Temperature Sensors

These sensors are thermistors, which are resistors whose values change with temperature. Under cold or hot engine, or cold ambient temperature conditions, compressor clutch engagement may not be desirable.

Wide Open Throttle Switch

Some vehicles with smaller engines are equipped with a Wide Open Throttle (WOT) switch. When the accelerator pedal is pressed all the way to the floor, this switch opens the electrical circuit to the compressor clutch to temporarily disable the compressor. This eliminates the load it places on the engine, as it is most often assumed that the pedal on the floor means it is more important to go fast at that moment than to remain cool inside the car. When the accelerator is released from the floor, the compressor clutch will re-enable the compressor.

Throttle Position Sensor

The throttle position sensor reports to the engine management computer on engine demand conditions. It works in a capacity like that of the wide open throttle switch.

Manifold Absolute Pressure (MAP) And Mass Airflow (MAF) Sensors

These are engine load sensors. The computer may decide to prevent clutch operation under conditions of high engine load.

Power Steering Pressure Switch

This switch is installed in the power steering system and reports on high pressure conditions. High pressure means that there is a load being placed on the engine by the power steering pump. The computer may decide to temporarily shut down the compressor to prevent engine stalling or low idle speed. It could also raise idle speed through control of an idle speed control device.

Drive Belts, Pulleys And Tensioners

Squealing noises from the engine compartment that increase in frequency as the engine rpm is raised, or when the A/C compressor is engaged, can usually be attributed to loose belt(s). In addition, pulley misalignment can cause the belt to enter the compressor pulley on an angle, also causing noise.

Check the compressor belt(s) for wear and proper adjustment as described under Preliminary Inspection in the A/C System Performance Testing section of this study guide. If replacement is necessary, loosen the belt tensioner or compressor pivot, move the tensioner or compressor to eliminate belt tension, and remove the belt. Never pry the belt from its pulley. It may be necessary to remove other accessory drive belts to gain access to the compressor belt.

Before removing a serpentine V-ribbed belt, make sure there is a belt routing diagram handy or draw one prior to belt removal, to prevent installation problems. Use a socket or wrench to tilt the automatic tensioner away from the belt, and then remove the belt from the pulleys.

After the belt is removed, spin the pulley to determine if it wobbles or has any noticeable bearing wear. Inspect the pulleys for chips, nicks, cracks, tool marks, bent sidewalls, severe corrosion or other damage. Check for hard objects such as small stones or sand that may become imbedded in the bottom of the pulley grooves.

When replacing belt(s), inspect the A/C compressor and its corresponding pulley(s) for improper alignment. Aligned pulleys reduce both pulley and belt wear, and vibration of engine components. If the belt pulleys are severely misaligned, look for improper positioning of the A/C compressor or its corresponding pulley, improper fit of the pulley or shaft, or incorrect components installed.

Install a new belt by correctly positioning it in its pulley grooves. Using the proper tools, move the compressor to tighten the belt, or in the case of automatically tensioned drives, move the tensioner to a position where the belt can be installed onto the pulleys. Always use manufacturer's tension recommendations.

Compressor Assembly

Knocking noises from the compressor usually indicate internal damage, especially on piston-type compressors. Although technically the compressor can be rebuilt, it is usually replaced. Always check the compressor mounting and brackets before condemning the compressor for noise. A loose mounting can cause knocking noises from the compressor area that may be mistaken for internal compressor noise. In addition, loose compressor mounting can cause misalignment of the pulleys.

To remove the compressor, first recover the refrigerant from the system using the proper equipment. Disconnect the electrical connectors from the compressor and remove the compressor drive belt. Disconnect the pressure hoses from the compressor and plug the hoses to prevent system contamination. Remove the compressor mounting bolts and lift the compressor from the engine compartment.

Before installing a compressor, add the manufacturer's recommended type and amount of lubricant. Install the compressor in the engine compartment and secure the mounting bolts. Remove the plugs from the refrigerant hoses and install them onto the compressor assembly, using new seals or O-rings.

Install the compressor drive belt and adjust if necessary. Reconnect the electrical connectors. Evacuate and recharge the A/C system and check for leaks. Finally, check system performance.

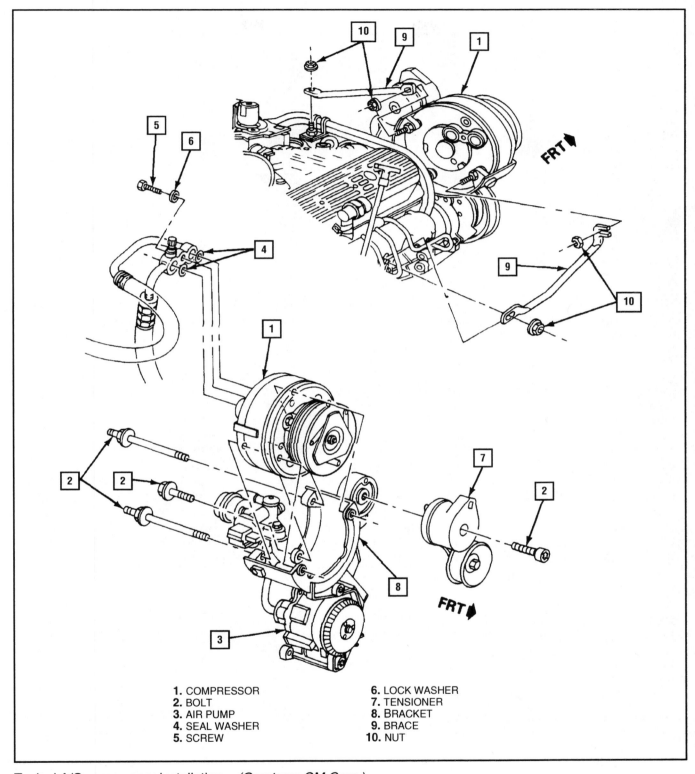

1. COMPRESSOR
2. BOLT
3. AIR PUMP
4. SEAL WASHER
5. SCREW

6. LOCK WASHER
7. TENSIONER
8. BRACKET
9. BRACE
10. NUT

Typical A/C compressor installation.   *(Courtesy: GM Corp.)*

Compressor Clutch

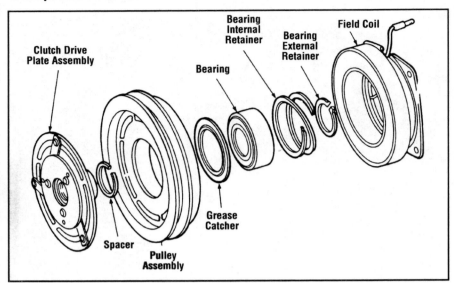

The stationary field coil creates a magnetic field when it receives an electrical signal. The field pulls the clutch drive plate into the pulley assembly so the engine-driven belt can rotate the input shaft of the A/C compressor.

An electromagnetic clutch provides the mechanical link between the pulley and the compressor input shaft whenever air conditioning is demanded. The compressor drive hub is usually found at the front of the pulley and is attached directly to the compressor driveshaft. A stationary electromagnetic coil is attached to the face of the compressor, behind the pulley.

When current flows through the coil windings, a magnetic field pulls the drive hub snug against the pulley. Now functioning as a unit, they drive the compressor as long as the coil is energized.

Compressor Clutch Inspection

Inspect the front of the compressor for oil, which could indicate a leaking front compressor seal. This would not only cause a refrigerant leak, but the oil could cause the compressor clutch to slip.

Connect manifold gauges and make sure there is adequate refrigerant in the system. Start the engine and turn on the A/C. If the compressor clutch does not engage, turn off the engine. Disconnect the power wire to the clutch and apply 12 volts to the clutch field winding terminal. If the clutch engages, then check the power supply to the clutch, including the system protection devices and electronic compressor controls.

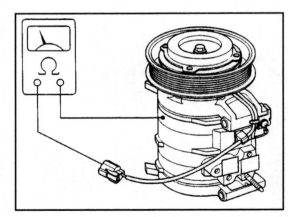

Measuring compressor clutch field coil resistance. *(Courtesy: Honda Motor Co., Ltd.)*

If the clutch does not engage, then check the clutch ground connection and coil resistance. If resistance is not within specification, then replace the coil or clutch assembly. If the compressor clutch engages noisily, suspect a defective compressor clutch plate, hub or rotor.

Compressor Clutch Replacement

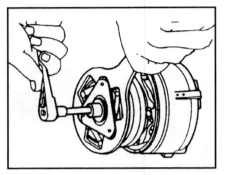

Hold the clutch hub with a suitable tool while the bolt or nut is removed. *(Courtesy: GM Corp.)*

Although most compressor clutch and drive pulley components can be serviced in the engine compartment, it is advisable to recover the refrigerant and remove the compressor from the vehicle. After the compressor is removed, clamp it in a suitable holding device with the clutch facing upward. If the clutch plate and hub are fastened to the shaft using a retainer such as a C-clip, remove the clip using the appropriate removal tool. If the clutch plate and hub are fastened to the shaft using a bolt or nut, hold the clutch plate using an appropriate clutch hub holding tool and remove the bolt or nut.

After the retainer has been removed, attach a clutch plate and hub puller into the hub assembly. Turn the center screw of the puller into the puller body until the clutch plate and hub have been separated from the shaft. Remove the Woodruff key from the hub and place it aside for future use.

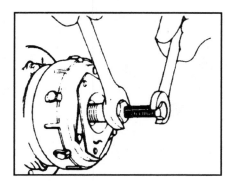

Removing the clutch plate and hub using a puller.
(Courtesy: GM Corp.)

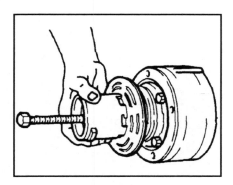

Removing the clutch rotor using a puller.
(Courtesy: GM Corp.)

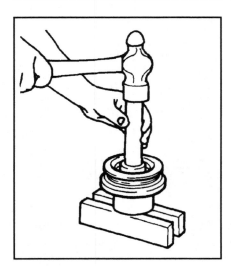

Removing the bearing from the clutch rotor.
(Courtesy: GM Corp.)

To remove the clutch rotor assembly, remove the rotor and bearing retaining ring and install the appropriate puller. Hold the puller in place and tighten the puller screw against the guide to remove the pulley rotor and bearing assembly.

After the rotor has been removed, inspect it to see if the bearing can be replaced. On some compressors, the bearing and rotor must be replaced as an assembly. However, if the bearing is replaceable, drive the bearing out of the rotor hub with a rotor bearing removal tool.

NOTE: At this time, it's a good idea to replace the compressor shaft seal, since the clutch, plate and hub assembly have been removed.

Next, remove the clutch coil by installing the appropriate puller on the front head of the compressor. Tighten the forcing screw against the puller pilot to remove the coil assembly.

When installing the coil, place the assembly on the front head of the compressor with the terminals in the proper position. Place a suitable installation tool over the opening of the clutch coil housing and align the installer with the compressor front head. Turn the installation tool forcing screw to force the clutch coil onto the front head until it is properly seated. Make sure the installation tool is properly aligned during installation.

Install the bearing into the clutch rotor (if applicable) by placing the rotor on a support. Align the bearing squarely with the hub bore, and using the installation tool, drive the bearing fully into the hub.

Now, install the compressor clutch rotor and bearing assembly on the front head. Position a rotor and bearing installation

tool directly over the rotor and tighten the center screw to force the assembly onto the compressor front head. Make sure the installation tool is properly aligned during installation. Once the assembly is properly seated, install the retainer ring.

When installing the replacement clutch and hub, place the Woodruff key into the hub groove. Make sure that the frictional surfaces of the clutch plate and clutch rotor are free of dirt, oil and debris before installation. Align the shaft keyway with the Woodruff key and place the clutch plate and hub assembly onto the compressor shaft.

CAUTION: Do not drive or pound on the clutch hub or shaft. Internal damage to the compressor can result.

Using a clutch plate and hub installation tool, press the hub onto the shaft. Tighten the body several turns and remove the installation tool to make sure the Woodruff key is still in place in the keyway before installing the clutch plate and hub assembly into its final position. After the clutch plate and hub have been seated, check the air gap between the frictional surfaces against manufacturer's specifications.

Measuring the clearance between the compressor clutch friction surfaces. *(Courtesy: GM Corp.)*

If the air gap is sufficient, remove the installation tool, and double-check for proper Woodruff key positioning. If the retainer is a C-clip, install the clip. If the retainer is a bolt or a nut, hold the clutch and hub with the appropriate tool, and install the bolt or nut. Torque to manufacturer's specifications.

If the compressor clutch components have been replaced with the compressor off the vehicle, reinstall the compressor and connect the pressure lines and electrical connectors. Evacuate and recharge the A/C system using the proper equipment, and check for leaks. Finally, check system performance.

EVAPORATOR, CONDENSER AND RELATED COMPONENTS

A/C Hoses, Lines And Fittings

Refrigerant is routed to the various components in the A/C system by rigid lines and flexible high-pressure hoses. Hoses are used to connect components with the compressor, to allow for engine movement. Most other components are connected with rigid lines, although hoses are sometimes used. Most modern hoses are made of reinforced rubber with a nylon inner layer as a barrier material to prevent refrigerant leakage. Most lines are made of aluminum. Generally, the line or hose of largest diameter is the one between the evaporator and compressor on the low side of the system. The smaller diameter lines connect the compressor to the condenser and the condenser to the evaporator on the high side. Often there is a muffler between the compressor and condenser to quiet the pumping noise of the compressor.

Inspect the refrigerant lines and hoses for leaks, kinks, dents and any other damage. When installing a new hose or line,

make sure it is routed properly and that all guides and retainers are in place, if equipped. Do not replace a line or hose with one that is longer or shorter than the original, as damage from vibration or interference with other components may result. The type of refrigerant used in the system must be considered when replacing refrigerant hoses, as some hoses are not compatible with both R12 and R134a refrigerants and their respective oils.

Hoses and lines are connected to components and one another using several types of fittings, including O-ring fittings, manifold fittings and spring lock fittings. Most all fittings use O-rings at the attachment ends. O-rings should be replaced each time a connection is disturbed and lubricated with refrigerant oil before installation. Replacement O-rings must also be selected with refrigerant compatibility in mind.

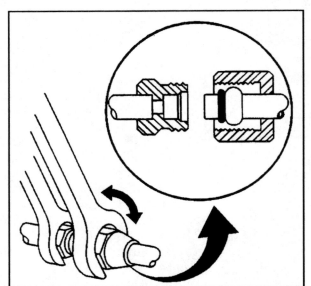

To prevent damage to refrigerant lines and A/C system components, a backup wrench should be used whenever disconnecting and connecting a refrigerant line fitting. *(Courtesy: GM Corp.)*

Spring Lock Fittings

Spring lock fittings require a special tool to disconnect them.

To disconnect spring lock fittings, a special tool is required. *(Courtesy: Ford Motor Co.)*

To disconnect a spring lock fitting, first properly recover the refrigerant from the system, then fit the tool over the fitting. Push the tool into the cage opening to release the female fitting from the garter spring, then pull the male and female fittings apart. Remove the tool from the fitting.

Remove and discard the O-rings, being careful not to scratch the tubing. Inspect the garter spring and remove it if broken or damaged. Clean the ends of the fittings.

Install a new garter spring, if removed. Lubricate new O-rings with clean refrigerant oil and install them. Lubricate the fitting ends with clean refrigerant oil, then push them together with a slight twisting motion. The fitting is properly connected if the garter spring is over the flared end of the female fitting. Evacuate and recharge the system, then check for leaks.

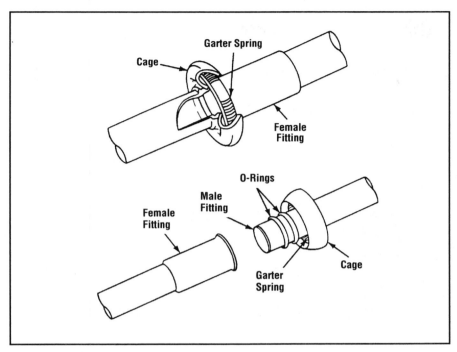

Spring lock fitting details.

Service Port Fittings

As described earlier, service valve fittings are of different diameters between the high and low side of the system and different styles for R12 and R134a systems. The high and low side fittings are different diameters to prevent connecting service hoses to the wrong fittings. The reason for the different fitting designs is to prevent cross contamination of systems, refrigerant supplies, and service equipment. The fittings are covered with caps also containing O-rings. Always re-install the caps after service, and replace any damaged O-rings in the caps. This is a common source of slow leaks, so make sure that the valves are seated properly and that caps aren't missing.

Filters

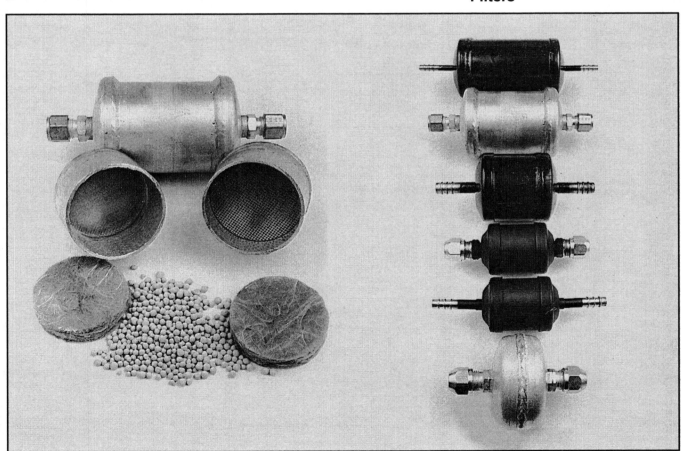

In-line filters come in many different designs. Many manufacturers recommend that filters be installed after a compressor failure to protect the new compressor from metal particles that may remain in the system.

Although not usually installed as original equipment, many vehicle manufacturers recommend installation of in-line filters in a system that has suffered a compressor failure. The main reason is for protection of the new compressor from metal chips or other debris that could be in the system from the original compressor failure. The other reason is that the debris could also clog orifice tube or expansion valve filters, or wedge in an expansion valve and keep it from operating properly. There are filters that fit into both the high and low sides of the system.

Condenser

The condenser is a heat exchanger much like a radiator. In fact, it is usually located just in front of the radiator on most vehicles. Air flow across the condenser is provided by an engine driven or electric motor operated fan, and at higher road speeds, by ram air.

The hot, vaporized refrigerant is pumped from the compressor into the condenser. As the refrigerant winds its way through the condenser coils, it loses much of its heat to the surrounding air through its tubes and fins. As it cools, the high-pressure vapor condenses into a warm, high pressure liquid.

There are three basic types of condensers: tube and fin, serpentine, and parallel flow. The tube and fin style has pipes that pass through fins, with U-shaped fittings on the ends of the pipes connecting one to the next. The serpentine condenser has a flat, continuous piece of tubing that snakes through the fins. This type is more efficient than the tube and fin design, and it's more compact. The parallel flow condenser is most similar to a radiator in its construction and is the most efficient of the designs in terms of heat transfer.

Condenser replacement is required if the unit leaks or if it is damaged or clogged. Suspect a defective condenser if high side pressures are excessive or if there has been a compressor failure and debris is suspected to be clogging the condenser. A restriction in the condenser is indicated by frost forming near the condenser outlet. Frost can also form on the condenser itself at the point of restriction in the condenser.

To replace a condenser, first recover the refrigerant from the system. Disconnect the negative battery cable and remove any components necessary to gain access to the condenser. Disconnect the refrigerant lines from the condenser and cap the lines to prevent system contamination. Remove the fasteners that secure the condenser and remove the condenser from the vehicle.

Measure the amount of oil found in the condenser that was removed, and then add the same amount of fresh refrigerant oil into the replacement condenser. If oil has leaked out of the system, use the manufacturer's recommended amount. Position the condenser in the vehicle and install the mounting fasteners. Tighten all fasteners to specifications. Using new, lubricated O-rings, connect the refrigerant lines. Install any components that were removed for condenser access. Reconnect the negative battery cable. Next, evacuate and recharge the A/C system and check for leaks. Finally, check system performance.

Receiver/Drier

As its name implies, the receiver/drier stores and dries the refrigerant. More accurately, a desiccant inside of it absorbs moisture from refrigerant. Receiver/driers are only used on systems that use expansion valves. They are located between the condenser and evaporator in the high pressure side of the system, ahead of the expansion valve.

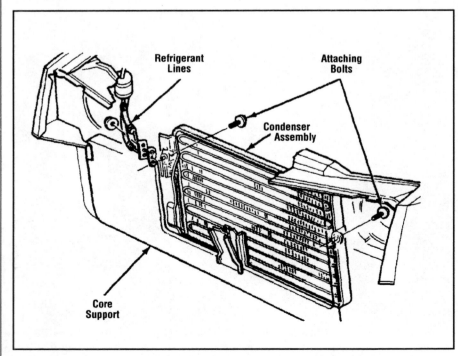

Typical condenser mounting. *(Courtesy: DaimlerChrysler Corp.)*

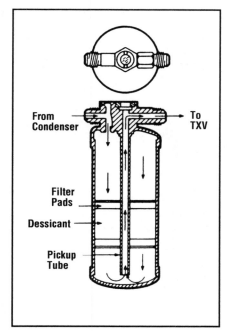

The receiver/drier is usually located on the output line of the condenser. The refrigerant enters the unit, flows through a desiccant, which helps keep moisture out of circulation, and then is routed to the expansion valve. The receiver/drier should be replaced if the system is left open or if major service is being performed, especially if the compressor is being replaced.

Inside the receiver/drier housing is a filter, a bag of desiccant (drying agent) and a pickup tube. If the air conditioning system has a sight glass, it is often located on the top of the receiver/drier.

In its 'receiver' function, the unit stores liquid refrigerant until the evaporator needs it. How long and how much refrigerant is stored depends on cooling demand. On hot, humid days, demand is high and refrigerant isn't stored long.

In its 'drier' function, the receiver/drier protects the rest of the system from the damaging effects of moisture. Water in the system can combine with refrigerant and lubricant, form corrosive substances, and even change the chemical composition of refrigerant and lubricant. The desiccant, which usually looks like very large granules of salt, is contained within a porous bag. This bag sometimes breaks, which allows the desiccant to leave the receiver/drier and flow throughout the system. This obviously renders it ineffective as a moisture absorbent.

The desiccant can only absorb and hold so much moisture. If too much water gets in the system, the desiccant must be replaced. In most cases, you have to replace the whole receiver/drier unit to achieve this. Desiccants are not universal. Different types must often be used with different refrigerants and lubricating oils.

The receiver/drier should be replaced if it leaks, if it is clogged, if the system has been left open for a period of time or if major system service has been performed, such as compressor replacement. Suspect a defective receiver/drier if desiccant is found in other parts of the system, if there is moisture or debris in the system, or if there is a significant temperature difference in the liquid line before and after the receiver/drier or there is frost on the receiver/drier, which would indicate a restriction.

To replace a receiver/drier, first recover the refrigerant from the system. Disconnect the negative battery cable and disconnect any electrical connectors from the receiver/drier. Remove any components necessary to gain access to the unit. Disconnect the refrigerant lines from the receiver/drier and cap the lines to prevent system contamination. Remove the fasteners that secure the receiver/drier and remove it from the vehicle. If equipped, remove any switches or sensors that are mounted on the receiver/drier.

If necessary, install any switches or sensors that were removed onto the replacement receiver/drier. Measure the amount of oil found in the receiver/drier that was removed, and then add the same amount of fresh refrigerant oil into the replacement receiver/drier. If oil has leaked out of the system, use the manufacturer's recommended amount. Position the receiver/drier in the vehicle and install the mounting fasteners. Tighten all fasteners to specifications. Using new, lubricated O-rings, connect the refrigerant lines. Install any components that were removed for receiver/drier access. Reconnect the electrical connectors to the receiver/drier, if necessary, and reconnect the negative battery cable. Next, evacuate and recharge the A/C system and check for leaks. Finally, check system performance.

Accumulator

On a system with an orifice tube rather than an expansion valve, the receiver/drier is substituted for by a component called an accumulator. The accumulator is usually located near the outlet of the evaporator. Refrigerant flowing out of the evaporator enters the accumulator to be stored, especially if it all has not vaporized in the evaporator. Because a liquid cannot be compressed, the accumulator ensures that only vaporized refrigerant reaches the compressor. The accumulator also contains a desiccant to keep the system free of moisture. Accumulators are similar in appearance to receiver/driers but usually bigger. Also, they never contain a sight glass. Their function is similar to that of receiver/driers in most every way, but they are located in the low pressure side of the system.

The accumulator should be replaced if it is leaking, if the

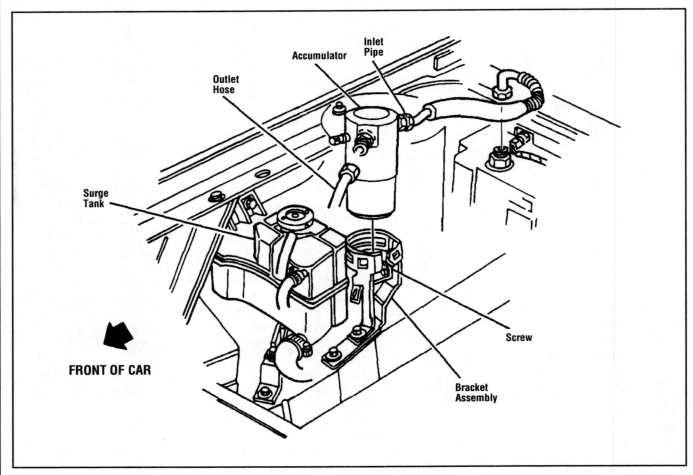

Typical accumulator mounting. *(Courtesy: GM Corp.)*

system has been left open for a period of time, or whenever any other major A/C system components are replaced. The accumulator cannot be serviced and can only be replaced as a unit.

To replace an accumulator, first recover the refrigerant from the system. Disconnect the negative battery cable and disconnect any electrical connectors from the accumulator. Disconnect the refrigerant lines from the accumulator and cap the lines to prevent system contamination. Remove the fasteners that secure the accumulator and remove it from the vehicle. If equipped, remove any switches or sensors that are mounted on the accumulator.

If necessary, install any switches or sensors that were

removed onto the replacement accumulator. Measure the amount of oil found in the accumulator that was removed, and then add the same amount of fresh refrigerant oil into the replacement accumulator. If oil has leaked out of the system, use the manufacturer's recommended amount. Position the accumulator in the vehicle and install the mounting fasteners. Tighten all fasteners to specifications. Using new, lubricated O-rings, connect the refrigerant lines. Reconnect the electrical connectors to the accumulator, if necessary, and reconnect the negative battery cable. Next, evacuate and recharge the A/C system and check for leaks. Finally, check system performance.

Orifice Tube

Refrigerant entering the evaporator must be metered, or sprayed in as a low pressure liquid at a controlled rate. If too much refrigerant enters the evaporator at too fast a rate, it can cause evaporator icing. If too little refrigerant enters the evaporator at too slow a rate, it can cause poor cooling performance. Also, the refrigerant's pressure must be kept low enough so that it will vaporize (boil) around the temperature of the vehicle's interior. The orifice tube acts as a restriction in the system, which creates the pressure drop. On its outlet side, pressure is lower than its inlet side. The orifice tube is usually located at the evaporator inlet.

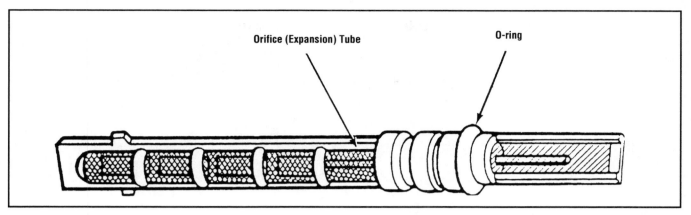

This is a typical orifice tube assembly. The actual tube is contained within a plastic housing made up mostly of a filter screen.

As the low pressure liquid refrigerant exits the orifice tube, it sprays into the evaporator. As the refrigerant's pressure drops, so does its temperature. The refrigerant is now colder than the air inside the vehicle so it readily boils, or vaporizes. It absorbs heat from the passenger compartment, which it carries away as it is drawn out to the compressor. However, the orifice tube has a fixed inside diameter and cannot change in response to evaporator temperature. When the cooling load is low, an orifice tube flows too much refrigerant and floods the evaporator with liquid refrigerant. Because of this, an orifice tube system always has an accumulator to catch and store the liquid refrigerant.

Air conditioning systems with orifice tubes cycle the compressor on-and-off to control refrigerant flow. When the temperature/pressure in the evaporator drops, the compressor is stopped until the temperature/pressure rises to a certain level, when compressor operation resumes. Because evaporator pressure and temperature are closely linked, the cut-out and cut-in signals can be provided by a temperature sensing thermistor located near the evaporator or a pressure switch mounted on the accumulator or low pressure hose.

Most orifice tubes look very similar to each other externally. Internally, the difference is the actual diameter of the opening inside the tube that the refrigerant passes through. This tube, often made of brass, has a very small inside diameter. (It could be as small as 0.050-in.). The external 'housing' of an orifice tube is usually plastic with a filter screen to trap debris so it doesn't plug the tiny inside diameter of the tube. There is also usually an O-ring seal on the external housing. This wedges the orifice tube in tightly against the inside walls of the portion of the A/C system plumbing it is contained in, which prevents refrigerant bypass.

The most common reason for replacing an orifice tube is if it is plugged. If there is a complaint that the A/C is not cold enough or not cold at all, and if the low side pressure is very low and there is frost on the line between the orifice tube and the evaporator, suspect a plugged orifice tube.

NOTE: On some vehicles the orifice tube cannot be removed from the line. If orifice tube replacement is required, a new line must be installed or a kit that provides a new line segment including the orifice tube can be installed.

A special tool is usually required to remove an orifice tube. To replace an orifice tube, first recover the refrigerant from the system. Disconnect the negative battery cable. Disconnect the liquid line from the evaporator inlet line and plug the liquid line to prevent contamination.

Pour a small amount of clean refrigerant oil into the evaporator inlet line to lubricate the line and orifice O-rings during removal. Engage the tangs on the orifice tube with the special tool. Hold the tool stationary and run the sleeve on the tool down against the evaporator inlet line until the orifice tube is pulled from the line. Do not twist or rotate the orifice tube in the line as it can break. Special tools are available to extract broken orifice tubes.

Lubricate the O-rings on the replacement orifice tube with clean refrigerant oil, then install it into the evaporator inlet line until it is seated. Using a new O-ring, connect the liquid line to the evaporator inlet line. Connect the negative battery cable. Evacuate and recharge the A/C system and check for leaks, then check system performance.

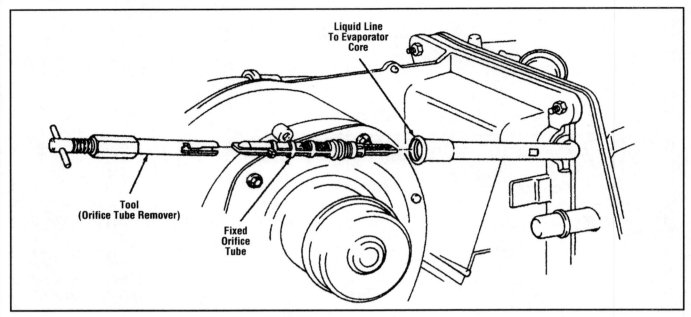

Fixed orifice tube removal.   *(Courtesy: Ford Motor Co.)*

Expansion Valve

Many A/C systems use a Thermostatic Expansion Valve (TXV) to restrict the amount of refrigerant entering the evaporator. Systems with expansion valves operate differently from those with orifice tubes. Although there are some expansion valve equipped systems that do utilize cycling clutch control, usually, instead of cycling the clutch on-and-off to control refrigerant flow, the expansion valve opens-and-closes as necessary to maintain proper evaporator pressure and temperature.

The TXV reduces the high pressure liquid refrigerant to low pressure liquid, which it meters to the evaporator at a controlled rate. There is a metered orifice at the expansion valve's outlet, but there is also a 'plunger' that opens-and-closes to control the amount of refrigerant that goes through the orifice to the evaporator.

The amount of TXV opening is determined by a signal it receives from the outlet side of the evaporator. A capillary tube bulb mounted to the outlet pipe of the evaporator is insulated against ambient heat. If outlet temperature is too high, the capillary bulb signals the TXV to allow more refrigerant to flow; if temperature is too low, the bulb signals the TXV to restrict the flow.

Although all expansion valves operate on a similar principle, they are not all identical. Usually they are spring loaded devices with a diaphragm that is linked to the plunger. Some diaphragms are internally equalized while others are connected to the low pressure side of the A/C system via an equalizer tube. Some expansion valves have a screen on the inlet side.

Expansion valves need devices

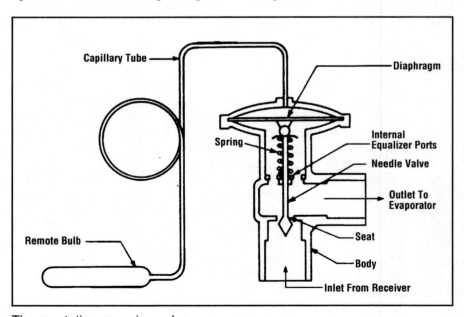

Thermostatic expansion valve.

to report to them what the conditions are at the evaporator. This is the job of the capillary tube. This tube is filled with gas that expands and contracts to move the diaphragm against its internal or external equalizing pressure. On the end of the capillary tube there is usually a sensing bulb that is in contact with the evaporator or the evaporator's outlet pipe. It is insulated by a special tape to prevent ambient air temperature from affecting its operation. Regular electrician's tape cannot be substituted for this special insulated tape.

As the temperature at the evaporator outlet increases, the pressure in the capillary tube increases. This pressure acts on the diaphragm, which in turn opens the expansion valve and allows more refrigerant to enter the evaporator. Conversely, when evaporator temperature decreases, pressure in the capillary tube decreases. Less pressure acts on the diaphragm, which in turn allows the expansion valve to close, and less refrigerant enters the evaporator. This dithering constantly controls the amount of refrigerant entering the evaporator, thereby controlling evaporator pressure and temperature.

On evaporators with large pressure drops between the inlet and outlet, an equalizing tube may be used between the evaporator outlet and the TXV. In essence, this equalizer eliminates the effect of the large pressure drop on TXV operation. These equalizers can be internal or external.

Expansion valves are usually non-serviceable. If one malfunctions, you must replace it. However, some are equipped with filter screens, and if this is the case, it should be cleaned whenever the system is opened for service of other components.

A TXV should be replaced if it becomes clogged or stuck in position due to debris, contamination or corrosion, or if the capillary tube is damaged. If the TXV is stuck closed, restricting the refrigerant flow, the air flow inside the vehicle will not be cold, the low and high side pressures will be low and there may be frost on the valve. If the TXV is stuck open, flooding the evaporator with excess refrigerant, the air flow inside the vehicle will not be cold and the system low side pressure will be high.

To replace a TXV, first recover the refrigerant from the system. Disconnect the negative battery cable. Remove the insulation covering the capillary tube and bulb and remove the capillary tube from its mounting. Disconnect the refrigerant lines from the TXV and cap the lines to prevent contamination. Remove the TXV from the vehicle.

Install the replacement TXV and connect the refrigerant lines using new O-rings lubricated with clean refrigerant oil. Properly position the capillary tube and bulb along with the insulation. Connect the negative battery cable. Evacuate and recharge the A/C system and check for leaks, then check system performance.

Evaporator

The evaporator is a heat exchanger not much different in appearance or design from a heater core, but with one main operational difference. Cool air passing over a heater core picks up heat from it and becomes warmer. Heat from the air passing over an evaporator is absorbed by it and the air becomes colder. The evaporator is aptly named because it reflects the fact that inside of it the refrigerant turns from a liquid to a gas (boils). Liquids boil sooner under low pressure than high pressure and refrigerant inside the evaporator has a pressure of about 30 psi.

Evaporator temperature should hover at 32° - 40°F (0° −4°C). At temperatures above this range, it does a poor job of cooling the inside of the vehicle. At lower temperatures, ice will form from condensation on the evaporator's fins, blocking air flow and rendering it ineffective as a heat exchanger. The key is to keep the evaporator temperature within the narrow 32° - 40°F (0° −4°C) range.

The evaporator is housed in a case, often the same one housing the heater core and blower. This case is usually called the plenum. The plenum also contains air routing and/or temperature blend doors, and is essentially a ductwork system. At the bottom of the evaporator case is a drain hole with a hose that directs the condensed water outside the vehicle. Make sure the drain is kept clear or stagnant water can collect and allow bacteria to grow, causing odors. A clogged drain can also cause the case to fill up with water and leak into the passenger compartment.

Replace the evaporator if it is leaking, clogged or corroded from moisture. Depending on the vehicle, it may be possible to remove the evaporator from the plenum with the plenum installed in the vehicle, or the entire plenum may have to be removed to access the evaporator. Begin by recovering the refrigerant from the system. Disconnect the negative battery cable. Disconnect the refrigerant lines from the evaporator and plug the lines to prevent contamination.

If the plenum is being removed and it also houses the heater core, drain the cooling system and disconnect the heater hoses. Label and disconnect the necessary electrical connectors and

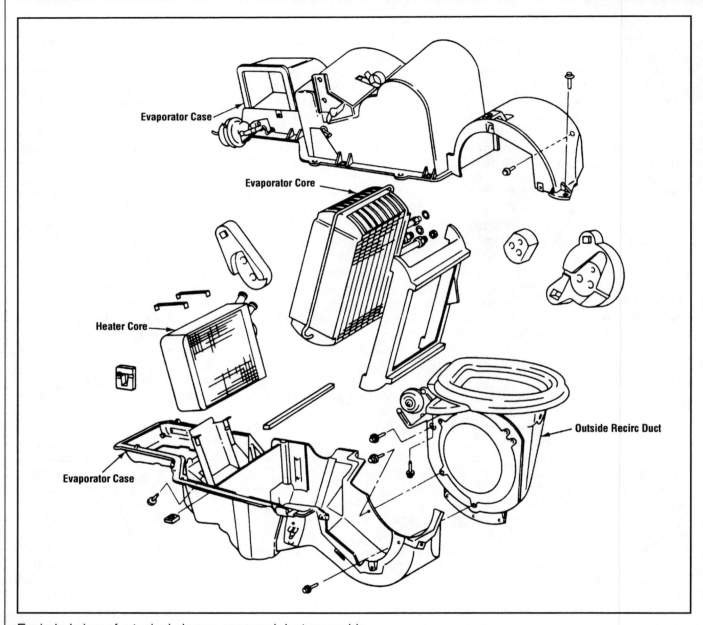

Exploded view of a typical plenum case and duct assembly.

vacuum hoses. Remove all other components necessary for evaporator or plenum removal, then remove the evaporator or plenum. If the plenum was removed, disassemble it as necessary to remove the evaporator.

Measure the amount of oil found in the evaporator that was removed, and then add the same amount of fresh refrigerant oil into the replacement evaporator. If oil has leaked out of the sys-

tem, use the manufacturer's recommended amount. If necessary, install the evaporator into the plenum. Install the evaporator or plenum into the vehicle. Install all components that were removed for access and connect the necessary electrical connectors and vacuum hoses.

If the heater core was removed with the plenum, connect the heater hoses and add coolant to the proper level. Connect the

refrigerant lines using new O-rings lubricated with clean refrigerant oil. Connect the negative battery cable. Evacuate and recharge the A/C system and check for leaks. Check system performance.

Evaporator Pressure/Temperature Controls

Evaporator pressure controls include the Suction Throttling

Valve (SVT) and the Pilot Operated Absolute (POA) valve. These devices maintain pressure in the evaporator by regulating the flow of refrigerant out of the evaporator, thereby controlling evaporator temperature. They are located in the suction line between the evaporator and compressor and are used in systems where the compressor operates continuously when the A/C is on.

The valve should be replaced if it sticks due to debris, contamination or corrosion. Symptoms of a valve that is stuck closed include high low side pressure, poor cooling and high evaporator pressure combined with low suction pressure. A valve that is stuck open is indicated by low evaporator pressure or a frozen evaporator.

To replace a valve, first recover the refrigerant from the system. Disconnect the negative battery cable. Disconnect the refrigerant lines from the valve and cap the lines to prevent contamination. Remove the valve from the vehicle.

Install the replacement valve and connect the refrigerant lines using new O-rings lubricated with clean refrigerant oil. Connect the negative battery cable. Evacuate and recharge the A/C system and check for leaks, then check system performance.

High-Pressure Relief Device

A high-pressure relief valve is used to release pressure in the system before excessive high-pressure can damage system components. When a predetermined pressure is reached, the valve opens, allowing refrigerant to escape until the pressure drops below the discharge point, when the valve closes. The high-pressure relief valve is located in the high side of the system.

When replacing a high-pressure relief valve, the replacement must have the same opening pressure specifications as the old one, unless the system is being retrofitted to R134a.

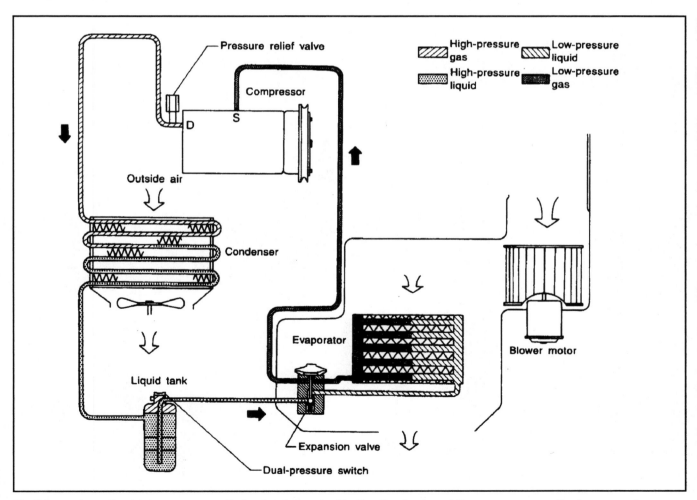

On this system, the high pressure relief valve is located in the line just past the compressor discharge port.

NOTES

HEATING AND ENGINE COOLING SYSTEMS
DIAGNOSIS AND REPAIR

HEATING AND ENGINE COOLING SYSTEM OPERATION

The function of the cooling system is to cause a rapid and even warm up of the engine and to keep it operating within a narrow temperature range. This keeps the engine at the temperature for the most efficient and safe operation. A cooling system is probably more accurately described as an engine temperature control system.

All engine cooling systems contain four major components, the water pump, thermostat, radiator, and heater core (these last two items are devices known as heat exchangers). As a convenient starting point, lets think of the water pump as the heart of the cooling system. In a conventional cooling system, the water pump moves the coolant through the engine block's water jackets, to the cylinder head(s), possibly through a passage in the intake

manifold, and then to the thermostat. As the coolant flows through the engine, it absorbs the heat that is generated in the engine's cylinders by the combustion process.

The thermostat, which is simply a valve that opens and closes depending on temperature, will open to allow coolant past it when the temperature of the coolant reaches a certain point. Cooling systems require a thermostat to control temperature and to assure quick warm up. If left to full flow, the cooling system would over-cool the engine. When cold, the thermostat restricts coolant flow from the engine to the radiator. A bypass system is used to permit coolant circulation through the engine to provide an even engine warm up. As the engine warms, the thermostat opens to permit coolant flow from the engine to the radiator. Most thermostats are designed to start opening around 190°F (88°C), and to be fully open around 210°F (99°C).

From the thermostat, the coolant flows through the upper hose to the radiator, and then through the internal tubes of the radiator, which have external fins attached to them. The heat from the coolant moves from the tubes to the fins, which provide a large surface area for heat dissipation to the cooler outside air. The cooled coolant then exits the radiator and returns to the water pump and engine to repeat the cycle.

The interior heater works in the same manner. Hot coolant is pumped through the heater core by the water pump, and heat from the coolant moves from the heater core to the passenger compartment as the blower fan forces air through the heater core.

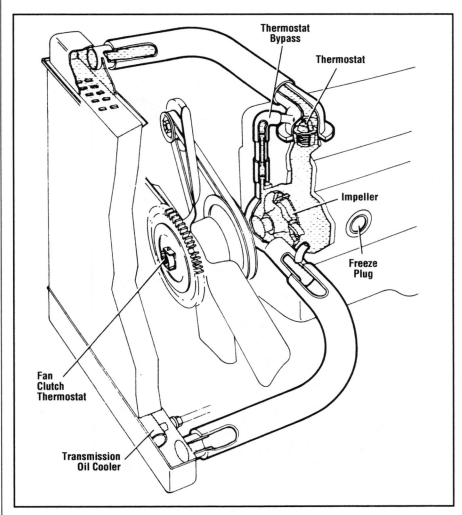

Thermostat Bypass

Thermostat

Impeller

Freeze Plug

Fan Clutch Thermostat

Transmission Oil Cooler

The cooling system will over-cool the engine if coolant flows unimpeded. When the engine is cold, the thermostat restricts coolant flow from the engine to the radiator, so that the engine can quickly come to normal operating temperature.

TEMPERATURE CONTROL DIAGNOSIS

The engine cooling system must be in good working order to ensure proper heating system operation. If coolant flow is restricted, it may not route through the heater core. If this is the case, outlet air temperature may be lower than anticipated, and interior heating will be insufficient.

If there is a complaint of not enough heat, first check to see if the cooling system needs servicing. Check for coolant leakage, both from the heater core and the engine compartment, and hose problems such as collapsing and blockage. Telltale signs of heater core leakage are if the floor of the passenger compartment is damp, or the windows are fogged. Fog that smears when wiped is a sign of coolant on the glass. You may also detect the odor of antifreeze in the passenger compartment.

Make sure the coolant level is OK and the thermostat is opening and closing properly. This allows the engine to heat the coolant to the proper temperature. Remember, a thermostat that is stuck open will cause lower-than-normal engine temperatures, causing the coolant to enter the heater core colder than it should be.

Start the engine and allow it to reach normal operating temperature. Check the temperature of the heater hoses going to, and from, the heater core. If the heater is working correctly, the return hose leading to the engine water pump will be nearly as hot as the feed hose. If the return hose is cooler, the heater core is generally either plugged or air-locked. An air pocket in the heater can usually be burped by loosening the outlet hose until coolant runs out while the engine is running.

If equipped, check the heater control valve for proper operation. Make sure the cable (if equipped) is connected and adjusted properly, and that it is not kinked or misrouted. If equipped with a vacuum-controlled valve, check the hose for vacuum and make sure the valve works when vacuum is applied. This valve is the critical temperature control component that allows the maximum amount of hot coolant to flow through the heater core.

Make sure that all heater ductwork is intact and routed to the proper flanges. Operate the blower through its entire speed range, leaving it on high. Operate the heater controls, making sure that when a particular mode is selected (such as defrost, floor vents, etc.) the outlet air is routed to that particular function. If not, check for proper operation of the air doors in the heater plenum. If the air doors are cable operated, make sure the cables are connected and adjusted properly, and that they are not kinked or misrouted. If the doors are vacuum or electronically operated, make sure there is vacuum or current to the actuator, and that the actuator func-

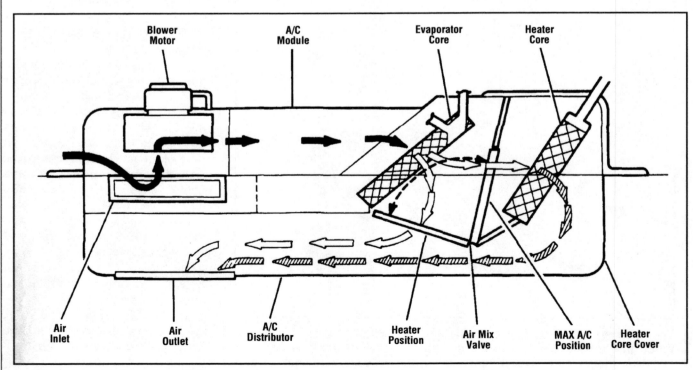

Air flow through a typical evaporator/heater core plenum. *(Courtesy: GM Corp.)*

tions properly. Note that if a door is shared by two functions (such as floor heat and defrost) it may bind halfway, routing heat in two different directions. This will give the impression that the heater is not performing properly.

COOLING SYSTEM INSPECTION

Begin cooling system inspection by checking the coolant level, then check coolant concentration using an antifreeze tester. The protection level should be at least −20°F (−30°C). Visually inspect the cooling system for problems. Check for signs of coolant leaks at all hose connections, core plugs (freeze plugs), head gasket(s), thermostat housing, water pump and radiator. Inspect all hoses for cracks, ballooning or brittleness and replace if necessary. If the hoses feel soft or mushy when they are squeezed, replace them.

Check the radiator cap rating to make sure it is the right one for the vehicle. Check the cap's relief valve spring action, and inspect the seal for brittleness. Check the filler neck on the radiator or surge tank mating surface.

Check the water pump drive belt for wear, glazing and belt tension. A slipping belt will not turn the pump impeller at the proper speed to circulate coolant. If the engine is equipped with a mechanical fan, a slipping belt will cause the fan to turn too slowly, not draw enough air through the radiator, and possibly cause the engine to overheat. Replace or adjust the belt as necessary.

Inspect the fan for missing, cracked or bent blades. If equipped with a fan clutch, check the back of the clutch for an oily film, which would indicate that fluid is leaking and replacement is necessary. Turn the fan and clutch assembly by hand; there should be some viscous drag, but

it should turn smoothly during a full rotation. Replace the fan clutch if it does not turn smoothly or if it does not turn at all. It should also be replaced if there is no viscous drag when hot or cold.

If the fan is electric, make sure it runs when the engine warms up and also when the A/C is switched on. Make sure the fan shroud is in place and not broken.

Start the engine and listen for unusual noises. A hammering sound may indicate a restriction in the water jacket or air in the system. Squealing noises indicate a bad belt or water pump bearing damage. Gurgling from the radiator may point to air in the system.

Cooling System Pressure Testing

Use a hand-held pump with a pressure gauge that is designed for cooling system testing. While the engine is cold, remove the pressure cap from the radiator or surge tank. Make sure the system is filled to capacity, then attach the tester. Pump it up to the rated system pressure and watch the gauge needle; it should

not drop rapidly. If pressure drops, check for leaks at the radiator and heater hoses, water pump, radiator, intake manifold, sensor fittings, water control valves and heater core. Repair leaks as required and retest.

If you can't spot the leak, it may be internal such as a head gasket, cracked cylinder head or cracked block. Inspect the engine oil for signs of coolant; if it is thick and milky, that's a dead giveaway. Start the engine and watch the tester gauge. If the pressure immediately increases, there could be a head gasket leak, but not into the crankcase. The coolant may be going out the tailpipe, however, which would be indicated by white smoke from the exhaust pipe and a somewhat sweet antifreeze odor in the exhaust. Remember that catalytic converters can mask small coolant leak symptoms because the converter super-heats the coolant into such a fine vapor that it is not noticeable.

Use the system tester's cap adapter to check the pressure cap. Pump it up to the cap's rating. It should hold for about 10

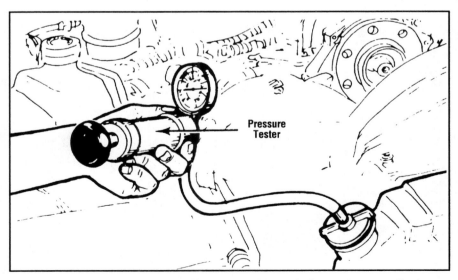

Pressure Tester

When pressure testing the cooling system, watch the gauge needle for an indication of a leak. Make sure all hose clamps are tight and that the heater core is not leaking. Remember that coolant can also leak into the engine and transmission lubricant systems.

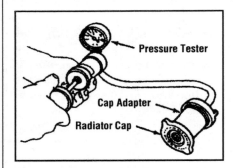

When pressure testing the radiator cap, the proper cap adapter must be used. The cap should be capable of holding the pressure recommended for the vehicle. Pressure test the cooling system at approximately the release pressure of the radiator cap.

seconds and then decrease just a bit. If it drops too much, replace the cap. If the pressure test exceeds the cap's rating by more than 3 psi, replace the cap.

THERMOSTAT

The thermostat's function is to allow the engine to come to operating temperature quickly and then maintain a minimum operating temperature. If the thermostat is good, the upper radiator hose should be hot to the touch after the engine has been idling and warm. If the hose is not hot, the thermostat is most likely stuck open, especially if there

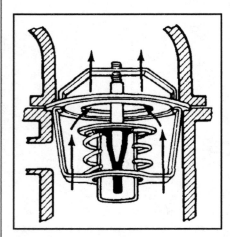

The thermostat is designed to open when the engine coolant reaches a specified temperature.

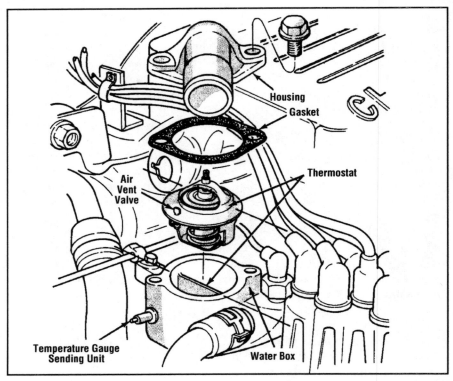

Typical thermostat installation.   *(Courtesy: DaimlerChrysler Corp.)*

has also been a complaint of poor heater performance. If the thermostat was stuck closed, the engine would quickly overheat.

To test the thermostat operation, remove the radiator cap while the engine is cold. Put a thermometer in the radiator fill neck and start the engine. Keep an eye on the coolant in the radiator and occasionally feel the upper radiator hose. When the hose gets warm, the coolant should be moving in the radiator. Check the thermometer. If it doesn't go above 150°F, the thermostat is either stuck open or missing.

The thermostat can be checked more precisely by removing it from the vehicle and submerging it a pan of water with a thermometer. Heat the water and observe the temperature when the thermostat opens. The opening temperature should match the thermostat's temperature rating. Remove the thermostat

from the water. The valve should close slowly when exposed to cooler ambient temperature.

To replace the thermostat, drain the cooling system and disconnect the hose from the thermostat housing. Remove the thermostat housing and remove the thermostat. Clean all gasket material from the sealing surfaces and check the surfaces for nicks or burrs.

Properly seat the thermostat in its flange on the engine. Make sure the heat sensing portion of the thermostat is installed so as to expose it to the hot coolant side. Using a new gasket, install the thermostat housing and torque the bolts to specification. Refill the cooling system, start the engine and check for leaks and proper operation.

RADIATOR

Coolant from the engine flows through a series of tubes in the radiator. These tubes are sur-

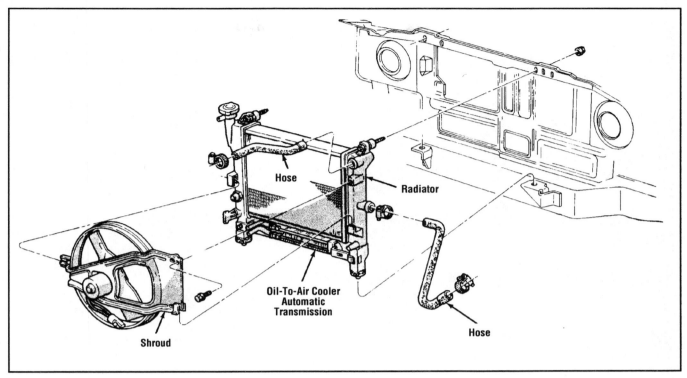

Typical radiator installation. *(Courtesy: DaimlerChrysler Corp.)*

rounded by a network of fins designed to direct air flow to the tubes. The cooled antifreeze is then circulated back through the engine in order to maintain proper operating temperature.

Clean the radiator fins of debris, bugs or leaves that may have been drawn in while driving. Make sure all fins are intact, and not bent so as to misdirect air flow. Distorted fins can be straightened using a suitable tool. However, be careful when straightening because the fins are very delicate.

Inspect the radiator for damage and any signs of leakage from the core tubes, radiator tanks and hose collars. If visual inspection and/or pressure testing indicates that radiator replacement is required, drain the cooling system and disconnect the hoses and transmission cooler lines, if equipped. Separate the radiator from the fan shroud and electric cooling

fan, if equipped, and remove the radiator mounting fasteners. Remove the radiator from the vehicle.

Transfer fittings and/or temperature sending units to the replacement radiator, as required. Position the radiator in the vehicle and tighten the mounting fasteners to specification. Install the shroud and electric cooling fan, if equipped. Connect the radiator hoses and transmission cooler lines, if equipped. Refill the cooling system, start the engine and check for leaks.

WATER PUMP

The water pump is mounted on the engine and driven by a belt. The pump employs an impeller fan designed to pump coolant throughout the engine via specially placed water jackets. While some water pumps are mounted directly behind the radiator fan and its pulley, others are

mounted independently on the front of the engine.

Check for a coolant leak at the water pump drain hole at the bottom of the pump. Check the water pump bearings by grasping the fan or pulley and attempt to move the impeller shaft back and forth. If there is any movement, the water pump bearings are defective. Replace the pump if it leaks or the bearings are defective.

To replace a water pump, drain the cooling system and disconnect the hoses from the pump. Remove the water pump drive belt and pulley. Remove any brackets or other components necessary for water pump removal. Remove the water pump mounting bolts and remove the water pump. Clean all gasket material from the sealing surfaces and check the surfaces for nicks or burrs.

Install the water pump using new gaskets and torque the

Typical water pump installation.
(Courtesy: GM Corp.)

mounting bolts to specification. Install any brackets or other components that were removed. Install the water pump pulley and the drive belt. Properly tension the belt, as required. Connect the coolant hoses to the water pump. Refill the cooling system, start the engine and check for leaks.

FLUSHING, FILLING AND BLEEDING THE COOLING SYSTEM

Engine overheating can be caused by a clogged cooling system. If you suspect that the system is clogged, drain it and then flush the system using one of the commercially available flushing kits. Flush the system according to the directions supplied with the kit.

All used coolants pick up heavy metals such as lead from the solder used in the assembly of heat exchangers, so drained coolant must either be disposed of properly or recycled.

After flushing, or whenever the cooling system has been drained for service, the system should be refilled with the vehicle manufacturer's specified coolant mixture. Ethylene glycol is the most widely used substance mixed with water to form engine coolant, although propylene glycol and some other substances are becoming popular. Not all ethylene glycol coolant is the same, however. Different ethylene glycol based coolants come with different corrosion inhibitor packages. There are the familiar brand name coolants that have been around for years, which are dyed green; GM's Dexcool, which is dyed orange or red; another that is dyed yellow and used in some Fords and other vehicles; as well as other colors for heavy-duty trucks and other applications. However, the color alone cannot be used to determine the type of coolant that's in the system or the container. For optimum system protection, use the type of coolant specified by the vehicle manufacturer.

A mix of 50 percent water/50 percent antifreeze is usually the most effective mixture, but some vehicle manufacturers may specify otherwise. This mixture lowers the freezing point while raising the boiling point, affording protection against boiling over. Drain and replace the coolant at the vehicle manufacturer's recommended interval, as the protective additives diminish in use.

When filling the cooling system, be aware that some vehicles have bleeder valves to release air trapped in the system and require that a specific bleeding procedure be followed. If there are no bleeders, to prevent air from becoming trapped in the system you can remove a hose from the highest point (usually at the heater core) and fill the system until coolant begins to come out at this point. Start the engine, and as soon as the level in the radiator drops, top it off and install the cap. Fill the reservoir to the indicated level.

Most all cooling systems in use today are equipped with a coolant reservoir. The radiator cap in the system functions as a two-way check valve: It has a limit that, once exceeded, allows the coolant to escape from the radiator and into the reservoir. This happens normally as the coolant heats up and expands. As the system cools, it creates a partial vacuum and sucks coolant from the reservoir or surge tank back into the radiator. It is a closed system where, ideally, no coolant escapes and no air gets into the cooling system. Air in the system contributes to corrosion.

When adding coolant to this type of system, add it to the reservoir, noting that the tank is usually marked with the proper coolant level. The overflow tank serves as a receptacle for coolant forced out of the radiator overflow pipe and provides for its return to the system. As the engine cools, the balancing of pressures causes the coolant to siphon back into the radiator.

COOLING FANS

Mechanical Cooling Fan

Most rear-wheel drive cars and trucks have belt-driven, mechanical fans equipped with a fan clutch. The fan clutch is designed to slip when cold and rotate the fan at certain maximum speeds when hot. Fan clutches improve gas mileage and reduce noise levels.

Inspect the fan clutch as described under Cooling System Inspection in this study guide. To test the fan clutch, attach a thermometer or electronic temperature probe to the radiator near the inlet and connect a timing light to the engine. Start the engine and strobe the fan to 'freeze' the blades; note the engine speed. When the engine

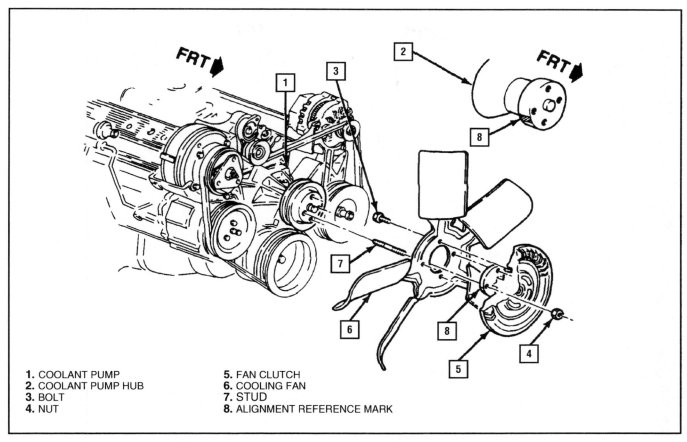

1. COOLANT PUMP
2. COOLANT PUMP HUB
3. BOLT
4. NUT
5. FAN CLUTCH
6. COOLING FAN
7. STUD
8. ALIGNMENT REFERENCE MARK

Typical mechanical cooling fan and fan clutch. *(Courtesy: GM Corp.)*

warms up (check the thermometer), the fan speed should increase and the blades will appear to be moving in the strobe light. As the temperature drops, the fan should slow down. A quick check of fan clutches is to shut down a hot engine, then observe how long it takes for the fan to stop spinning. A properly operating clutch should stop the fan from spinning within two seconds. Replace the fan clutch if it fails inspection or testing.

Electric Cooling Fan

Many vehicles, especially those with transverse engines, use electric cooling fans. Besides not needing a belt to drive them, electric fans conserve energy since they run only when needed.

When the engine slightly exceeds proper operating temper-ature, the electric fan should come on. It may cycle on and off as the coolant warms and cools. On most vehicles, the fan also should run whenever the A/C is switched on. (Some vehicles have two fans with one dedicated to the A/C system. That one may not run for engine cooling alone.)

If the fan doesn't run, check for power at its connector using a test light. If there is power, the fan motor is faulty. If there is no power, the problem may be a blown fuse, a bad relay, the fan's temperature switch, the engine coolant temperature sensor, the computer controls or wiring. In most cases, the fan motor can be replaced by removing the entire assembly, and then removing the fan from its motor. Use caution not to damage the radiator fins or core tubes when removing the fan.

HEATER CONTROL VALVE

Although they are becoming less common, many vehicles still have water valves in the engine compartment to stop the flow of coolant to the heater core when it is not needed. Start the engine and run it until it reaches normal operating temperature. Switch the heater to its hottest setting and feel the hose between the heater control valve and the heater core. It should feel about the same temperature (hot) as the hose without the heater control valve. If both hoses are not equally as hot, chances are the heater control valve is inoperative. Make sure the cable (if equipped) is connected to the valve and adjusted properly, and that it is not kinked or mis-routed. If equipped with a vacuum-controlled valve, check the hose for vacuum and make sure the valve works when the vacuum is applied.

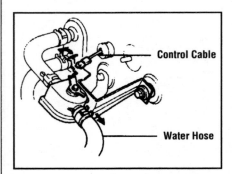

Typical cable-operated heater control valve.
(Courtesy: Toyota Motor Corp.)

If the valve is leaking or inoperative, it must be replaced. Drain the cooling system, then disconnect the vacuum hose or cable from the valve. Disconnect the heater hoses and remove the valve. Inspect the condition of the heater hoses and clamps and replace as necessary.

Connect the valve to the heater hoses, noting the proper coolant flow direction, and secure with the clamps. Reconnect the vacuum line or cable. Refill the cooling system. Start the engine and allow it to warm up to operating temperature. Turn the heater to its highest temperature and check for proper operation.

HEATER CORE

As mentioned earlier, moisture on the passenger floor or a slimy film on the windows is a sign of heater core leakage. You can test the heater core using the cooling system pressure tester and an adapter to connect to the heater core inlet pipe. After capping the outlet, pressurize the core and replace it if it doesn't hold pressure. If, during the cooling system inspection it was found that the return hose leading to the water pump was much cooler,

the heater core is most likely plugged or air bound. An air bound heater can be burped by loosening the outlet hose until coolant runs out while the engine is running. However, a plugged core must be corrected by reverse flushing or replacement.

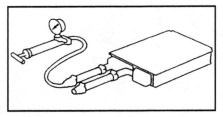

Pressure testing a heater core.
(Courtesy: Ford Motor Co.)

Replace the heater core if it is leaking or plugged. Depending on the vehicle, it may be possible to remove the heater core from the plenum with the plenum installed in the vehicle, or the entire plenum may have to be removed to access the heater core. Disconnect the negative battery cable and drain the cooling system. Disconnect the heater hoses from the heater core.

If the plenum is being removed, label and disconnect the necessary electrical connectors and vacuum hoses. Remove all other components necessary for heater core or plenum removal, then remove the heater core or plenum. If the plenum was removed, disassemble it as necessary to remove the heater core.

If necessary, install the heater core into the plenum. Install the heater core or plenum into the vehicle. Install all components that were removed for access and connect the necessary electrical connectors and vacuum hoses. Connect the heater hoses to the heater core. Connect the negative battery cable. Refill the cooling system. Start the engine and allow it to warm up to operating temperature. Turn the heater to

its highest temperature and check for leaks and proper operation.

NOTES

OPERATING SYSTEMS AND RELATED CONTROLS DIAGNOSIS AND REPAIR

MANUAL HEATING, VENTILATING AND A/C SYSTEMS

System Operation

Vacuum and mechanical controls are combined with electrical controls to operate the Heating, Ventilation and Air Conditioning (HVAC) system. The items being controlled are activated by vacuum, cables, electricity or any combination of these. The instrument panel controls may operate vacuum switches to select the routings to the various vacuum motors that control A/C, defrost and heat modes. They may also be connected to cables that control a door or valve's position, or they can be electrical switches or potentiometers that can control electric motors or vacuum solenoids.

Controlling the temperature of the air entering the passenger compartment is usually achieved by means of a door in the plenum assembly, often referred to as the blend door. The door's position is controlled by a cable or small electric motor. The temperature of the air entering the passenger compartment can also be controlled by a heater control valve (water valve) mounted in the hose to the heater core. The heater control valve controls the flow of hot coolant through the heater core. Its position can also be controlled by a vacuum motor or cable.

Air routing is controlled very much the same way as temperature. Cable, vacuum, or electric motor operated doors inside the plenum assembly either open or block passages or ducts to dash vents, floor outlet, windshield defroster, etc. depending on which panel control position the driver has selected. Air can enter the HVAC system from either the interior of the vehicle ('RECIRC'), or from the outside ('FRESH'). Inside a vacuum motor housing is a spring loaded vacuum diaphragm, one side of which is connected to the vacuum source. The other side is attached to an arm that moves the air door.

System Diagnosis

Complaints of insufficient cooling or heating, or improper air routing, can often be traced to problems with vacuum or mechanical controls. Many failures or partial malfunctions of air conditioning systems can be caused by controls that are out of adjustment. Also, vacuum leaks or disconnected hoses will cause air doors to stay in the wrong position. To diagnose the positions of the doors in relation to the positions of the control head levers, a good air conditioning diagram is necessary.

If the problem seems to lie with an electrical device, check the necessary fuses, relay, diodes and wiring connections. Verify that the blower works at all speeds. Common sense will tell you a lot about the condition of electrical parts. For example, if the blower works on one speed only, you know that the blower motor is OK. The trouble then, would have to be in the switch or the resistor. For slower speeds, current is routed through one or more resistors in a resistor block. It is often found in the plenum where air flow can keep the resistor coils cool. Failure to work on one or more resistor speeds means that a portion of the resistor assembly is probably burned out or the high speed relay is defective.

On some vehicles, the mode doors are moved by DC motors that push or pull levers as necessary. Total failure may indicate a blown fuse, but if individual components malfunction, check for power to the motor and check the motor itself. Occasionally, the selector switch may be at fault, but this is less common.

If problems arise concerning air routing or temperature control, keep in mind that vacuum leaks are usually caused by bad hoses. It is more unusual to find a bad vacuum motor or switch. Vacuum is often maintained in the system by a vacuum reservoir. The reservoir may have a check valve in its supply hose, or the check valve may be part of the reservoir. If, during hard acceleration, air routing changes by itself, it's probably due to a leak in the system or a faulty check valve. A complaint that the mode shifts from the floor to defrost at wide open throttle is evidence that the system isn't holding vacuum. Hissing sounds also point to vacuum leaks. Some vacuum operated doors also have an adjustment in the length of the arm that attaches the door to the diaphragm.

Control cables usually have an adjustment at the end opposite to the control panel. Air doors that are operated by cables should be adjusted so that the doors shut tightly enough to stop air flow. This adjustment is made in most cases by shifting the cable housing in its clamp bracket near the door. Many cables today are self-adjusting and if there is a problem with operation, the cable may have become disconnected from the lever to which it was attached.

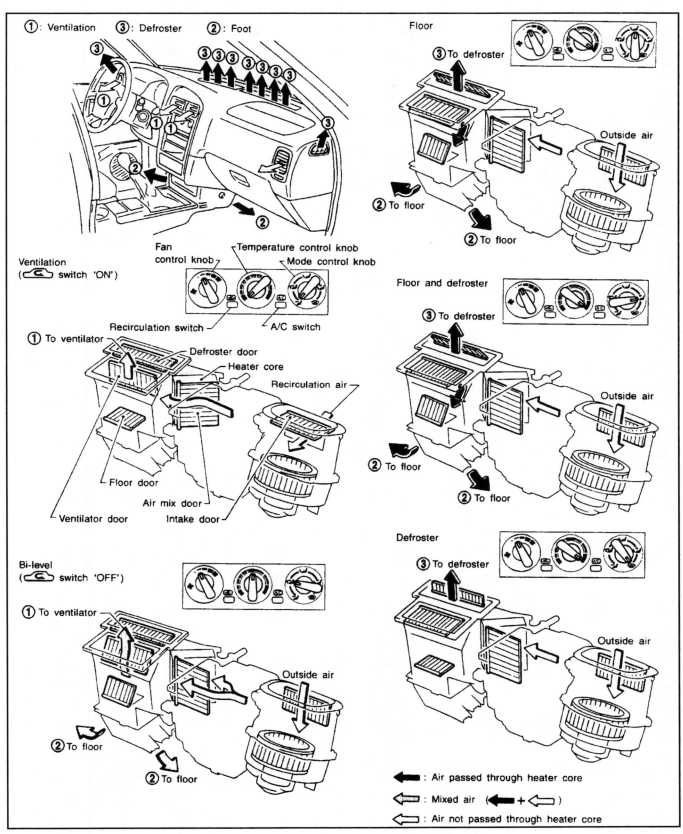

①: Ventilation   ③: Defroster   ②: Foot

Floor

③ To defroster

② To floor

② To floor

Outside air

Ventilation
(⟲ switch 'ON')

Fan control knob

Temperature control knob

Mode control knob

Recirculation switch

A/C switch

① To ventilator

Defroster door

Heater core

Recirculation air

Floor door

Air mix door

Intake door

Ventilator door

Floor and defroster

③ To defroster

② To floor

② To floor

Outside air

Bi-level
(⟲ switch 'OFF')

① To ventilator

Outside air

② To floor

② To floor

Defroster

③ To defroster

Outside air

◀ : Air passed through heater core

⟸ : Mixed air (◀ + ⟸)

⟸ : Air not passed through heater core

This diagram illustrates the air flow through the HVAC system. It shows the position of the doors in relation to the various control head positions. *(Courtesy: Nissan Motor Co., Ltd.)*

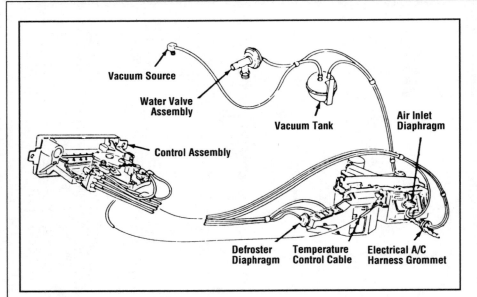

A/C systems acquire the control vacuum from a vacuum reservoir equipped with a check valve. The vacuum supply of this manual A/C system is routed from the reservoir to the dashboard control panel, where the mode selection lever distributes the vacuum signal to the appropriate plenum door vacuum servos and the heater hot water valve. The blower motor speeds are selected by a switch and a relay, and the temperature blend door is operated by a cable.

If control cables must be replaced, it is usually easier to drop the control panel out of the dash than to try to fit a new cable with the panel in place. Also, replacing a vacuum control switch on the control panel usually means the entire panel must be replaced as a unit.

Some interior air 'problems' may be caused by operator error. For instance, if the windows fog in cool weather, the motorist may be selecting RECIRC believing it best to keep the warm air inside. In fact, he or she is recirculating moisture laden air, and the windows will clear if fresh air is chosen.

Electrical Components

Blower Motor

If the blower motor doesn't work, check the fuse or circuit breaker, and check for voltage at the connector at the resistor block. Generally, if one or two of the blower speeds don't work, the

problem is a faulty resistor. If the high speed doesn't work, the problem could be the high-speed relay or a fuse. Don't overlook the switch on the dashboard or the ground for the blower motor. If the blower is too slow at all speeds, perform a current draw test to see if the windings or brushes are bad. Noises from the blower could point to a bad bearing or debris in the fan.

Note that blown fuses or breakers most often indicate a short circuit in the wiring. However, a short can sometimes occur in the blower motor itself. It is obvious that for the motor to work, two things are necessary, power (voltage) to the motor, and continuity to ground. So, the first thing to check for is voltage available at the motor. While a test light will indicate whether voltage is present, a DMM will indicate how much voltage is present.

To test for proper voltage, place the panel selector levers in the manufacturer's recommended positions and insert the probes of a DMM into the back of the connector at the blower motor. Check the measured voltage against manufacturer's specifications.

To test for blower motor current draw, disconnect the blower motor wire connector and connect a DMM (in the amps position) between the positive terminal on the motor and the corresponding terminal of the wire connector. Connect a jumper wire between the ground terminal on the motor and the corresponding terminal of the wire harness connector.

Place the panel selector levers in the manufacturer's recommended positions and start the engine.

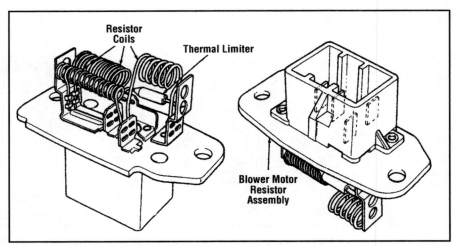

Typical blower motor resistor. *(Courtesy: Ford Motor Co.)*

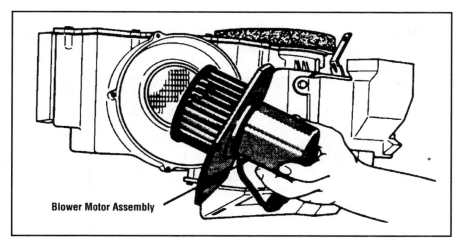

Typical blower motor installation. *(Courtesy: DaimlerChrysler Corp.)*

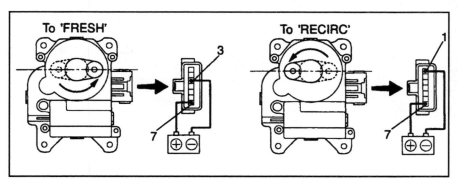

This servomotor is tested by applying 12 volts to terminal 7 and grounding terminal 3. The motor arm should then rotate to the 'FRESH' position. When terminal 1 is grounded the arm should rotate to the 'RECIRC' position. *(Courtesy: Toyota Motor Corp.)*

Condition	Fan operation (Fan speed)
Engine coolant temperature 88 °C (190 °F) or below	Rotate (Low speed)
Engine coolant temperature 98 °C (208 °F) or above	Rotate (High speed)
Refrigerant pressure is less than 1,520 kPa (15.5 kgf/cm^2, 220 psi)	Rotate (Low speed)
Refrigerant pressure is 1,520 kPa (15.5 kgf/cm^2, 220 psi) or above	Rotate (High speed)

An example of condenser fan operating specifications. *(Courtesy: Toyota Motor Corp.)*

Operate the blower at all speeds, recording the current draw for each speed. Compare with manufacturer's specifications.

Actuators And Servomotors

As explained earlier, electric actuators and servomotors are used in many systems to move air doors within the plenum, opening or blocking plenum passages. An actuator may directly operate a door or, when activated, may operate a vacuum motor, which in turn operates the door.

There are two-position actuators, which open or close, and continuous position actuators that can stop anywhere within a range. The latter are usually used for temperature blend door operation.

If there is a function or temperature problem caused by a malfunctioning air door, first make sure that there is power to the actuator. If there is no power, check the circuit back to the control head. If there is power to the actuator, then the actuator should be tested. Refer to the manufacturer's service information for specific testing procedures.

Condenser Fan

Some vehicles have a separate cooling fan for the condenser. The fan may have low-and-high speed operating modes. Some vehicles have two fans, with one being the low speed fan and the other the high speed fan.

Inspect the fan for missing, cracked or bent blades. Make sure the fan shroud is in place and not broken.

If the condenser fan doesn't run at all when the A/C is on, check for power at its connector using a test light. If there is power, the fan motor is faulty. If there is no power, the problem may be a blown fuse, a bad relay, the A/C pressure switch, the engine coolant temperature sensor, the computer controls or wiring.

Even if the condenser fan runs, refer to the factory service information to determine what constitutes proper fan operation. For example, the specifications may state that a two-speed fan should run at low speed if the engine coolant is below a certain temperature and the refrigerant is below a certain pressure, and run at high speed when that coolant temperature or refrigerant pressure is exceeded.

In most cases, the fan motor can be replaced by removing the entire assembly, and then removing the fan from its motor. Use caution not to damage the condenser fins or core tubes when removing the fan.

Potentiometer

Some vehicles have a potentiometer located in the HVAC control panel that relays the position of the temperature control lever to the ECM. The information is processed by the ECM and air conditioning output is regulated accordingly.

To test the potentiometer, locate the air conditioning control module. Connect a Digital Multimeter (DMM) switched to the ohms position across the potentiometer wires at the end of the module connector. Check the resistance of the potentiometer while moving the temperature control lever. Check the readings against manufacturer's specifications.

If the readings are not within specifications, replace the potentiometer. Disconnect the negative battery cable and remove the HVAC control head from the instrument panel. Disconnect the potentiometer wiring and remove it from the HVAC control head.

Compressor Clutch Controls

As previously discussed, cycling the compressor clutch is a method of controlling evaporator pressure and hence, its temperature. Whenever pressure approaches the high limit, the controls simply switch off the clutch until pressure drops. The clutch is turned off-and-on auto-

matically to prevent the evaporator from icing up. During operation, the clutch may cycle on-and-off several times each minute. As the change in heat load on the evaporator affects system pressures, the compressor cycling rate automatically changes to achieve the desired temperature. However, if the clutch cycles rapidly, it may be a sign of low refrigerant charge.

It is important to visually inspect the wiring and connectors to the various cycling and protection devices to make sure they are intact. Check for loose or broken wire connections, and damaged terminals. Ensure that all grounds are clean and making good contact.

The A/C electrical circuit must be opened or closed on demand from the system, or by the driver. Current will flow only in a closed circuit. In the case of the A/C compressor, the system must be performing at its optimum in order for the circuit to close, and the compressor clutch to engage. So, proper operation of all compressor clutch control switches is crucial to maintaining system performance levels.

A/C Clutch Relay

The relay is composed of a coil and a set of contacts. When current is passed through the coil, a magnetic field is formed, and this field causes the contacts to move together, completing the circuit. Most relays are normally open, preventing current from passing through.

The operation of the A/C clutch relay is directly affected by the A/C switch input circuit. When the switch is turned on, high pressure, low pressure, and temperature switches sense the correct conditions, and the relay opens to complete the circuit to the compressor clutch. However, any changes in pressure or tem-

perature sensed by the control switches that would indicate an out-of-range condition will shut off current to the relay, and disengage the compressor clutch.

Thermostatic And Pressure Switches

To cycle the compressor, some systems use a thermostatic switch. It has a capillary tube attached to the evaporator outlet or inserted between the evaporator core fins to sense the temperature. This capillary is attached to a switch that opens and closes as necessary to cycle the compressor. Most thermostatic switches are factory-set and not adjustable. If the switch is defective, the compressor clutch will cycle on-and-off quickly.

The more modern controls use a thermistor, which reacts faster than a mechanical thermostat to sense temperature changes. This keeps the temperature constant, as opposed to the temperature swings that are typical of mechanical thermostats. Additionally, thermistors do not need the constant air flow necessary to operate mechanical thermostats.

Although some orifice tube systems use a thermostatic switch to control compressor clutch cycling, others use a pressure cycling switch. It senses the low side pressure (which is directly proportionate to temperature) near the evaporator outlet. Usually the pressure cycling switch is found on the accumulator, and is often mounted in a Schrader fitting so it can be replaced without the loss of refrigerant. When system pressure is low, the switch opens; when it is high, the switch closes. The more heat the refrigerant picks up in the evaporator core, the higher the pressure becomes.

On expansion valve systems, the compressor is switched on around 25 psi and off about 10

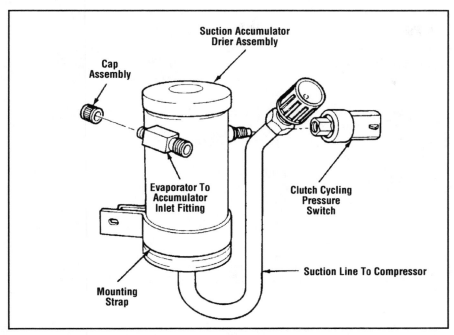

Typical pressure cycling switch mounting location.
(Courtesy: Ford Motor Co.)

psi. Orifice tube systems usually switch on around 45 psi and turn off at 25 psi. Since system pressure is quite low during cold weather, the pressure cycling switch keeps the compressor from running when it isn't needed. It also protects the compressor from damage should the refrigerant charge escape.

Low-Pressure Cutout Switch

The low-pressure cutout switch may be found in either the high or low side of the system, but its function is the same: it disengages the compressor clutch if the pressure drops below a preset level, keeping the compressor from being destroyed due to lack of lubrication, which normally flows with the refrigerant. Whenever there is a leak of refrigerant, oil leaks out as well.

To check the low-pressure cutout switch, disconnect the electrical connector and connect a jumper wire across the terminals. Start the engine and engage the A/C system. If the compressor engages after a brief period, suspect a defective low-pressure cutout switch. If the compressor does not engage, the wiring, fuse, or ambient temperature switch may be defective. If the clutch engages, connect a manifold gauge set, read the compressor discharge pressure and compare with manufacturer's specifications. At a specified pressure and ambient temperature, the switch should engage the compressor.

Recover the refrigerant using the proper equipment before servicing the switch. Disconnect the negative battery cable and the electrical connector from the switch. Remove the switch and its O-ring from its mounting. Install the replacement switch with a new O-ring. Connect the electrical connector and the negative battery cable. Next, evacuate and recharge the A/C system and check for leaks. Finally, check system performance.

High-Pressure Cutout Switch

Like the low-pressure cutout

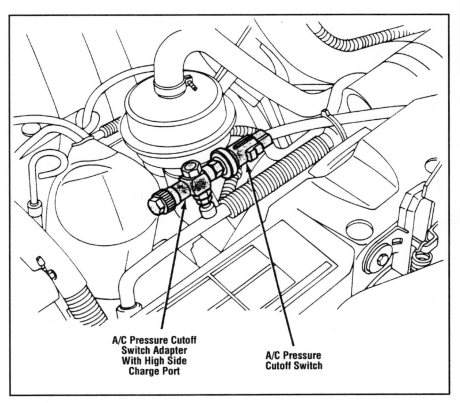

A compressor high-pressure cutout switch along with a service port.

switch, the high-pressure cutout switch protects the compressor from damage. It breaks the circuit to the compressor clutch if it detects pressures above a preset level. This switch is usually located in the high-pressure side of the refrigeration circuit.

A quick way to check the high-pressure cutout switch operation is to connect the manifold gauge assembly, start the engine and engage the A/C system. To create a high-pressure situation, restrict air flow through the condenser. The compressor should disengage once the pressure reaches the threshold of the switch calibration.

To replace the switch, disconnect the negative battery cable and the electrical connector to the switch. Remove the switch from the valve and discard the O-ring. Install the replacement switch with a new O-ring; connect the electrical connector and the negative battery cable. Finally, check system performance.

Thermal Limiter

Older General Motors systems used a remote-mounted, thermal limiter in conjunction with a superheat switch on the back of the compressor, to disengage the compressor clutch in the event of low refrigerant charge. When the superheat switch engages, electric current to a heater in the thermal limiter heats up a fuse, which then melts and breaks the circuit to the compressor clutch coil.

Early thermal limiters were sensitive to sudden pressure changes, but were redesigned to blow slower. Thermal limiters cannot be reused. However, they should only be replaced after the underlying cause of failure has been repaired.

Electronic Controls

HVAC control is increasingly being handled by computers. Sensors installed in the system report to the ECM, which then sends the command to cycle the clutch. Thermistors—resistors whose values change rapidly with temperature—are the most common type of sensors.

Some electronic engine controls have a direct relationship to A/C system operation. The goal is to optimize engine operation while minimizing the impact on A/C performance. Therefore, some engine sensors are also used in a dual capacity. While they inform the ECM of critical engine operating parameters, others combine to control operation of the A/C system in certain instances.

For instance, if an A/C belt becomes loose, a compressor rpm sensor can relay slower-than-normal pulley revolution to the ECM. The ECM then compares this rotation with the engine rpm, and disengages the compressor clutch if the variance is too high. The compressor rpm sensor can be located on or inside the compressor. These sensors are of the magnetic type, similar to a crankshaft position sensor.

On some vehicles, the vehicle speed sensor will inform the ECM that it has reached an acceptable speed to turn off the electronically controlled cooling fan. Since enough ram air is supplied at higher vehicle speeds, it is not necessary to run the cooling fan. As the vehicle slows down and ram air decreases, the speed sensor will tell the ECM to activate the cooling fan.

The coolant temperature sensor performs a similar function, only it senses when the coolant temperature has reached a level where the engine cooling fan should be turned on. The sensor changes value with temperature, and in some cases, tells the ECM to disengage the compressor clutch when an overheat condi-

tion is present. When coolant temperature has stabilized, the coolant temperature sensor informs the ECM, and the ECM re-engages the compressor clutch.

The wide open throttle switch or throttle position sensor tells the ECM to open the circuit to the compressor clutch when critical engine speed is in demand. The switches temporarily disable the compressor, eliminating the load it places on the engine. After acceleration, the switches inform the ECM that throttle demand has been reduced, and the ECM then engages the compressor clutch.

When a sensor malfunctions, a fault code is generated. The fault code is stored in the ECM memory. Active fault codes indicate a current problem of some kind. Inactive fault codes suggest a problem that may be temporary, or a problem that has been repaired or corrected since being stored in memory. Inactive fault codes may be helpful in finding intermittent problems. On some vehicles, information codes are generated when a specific function is active (air conditioner on, for instance).

Fault codes usually only indicate which circuit the problem is in; they don't necessarily indicate which component in the circuit has failed. The problem could be caused by a loose connection, improper modification, or a broken wire, so perform a thorough inspection when diagnosing a malfunction. Ensure that all grounds are clean and making good contact. If basic mechanical and electrical checks fail to locate the problem, follow manufacturer's electronic system test procedures.

Vacuum Actuators

As stated earlier, the vacuum actuator contains a spring-loaded diaphragm, one side of which is connected to the vacuum source. The other side is attached to an arm that moves the air door. Leaks or disconnected hoses will cause the doors to stay in the wrong position. To diagnose the positions of the doors in relation to the positions of the control

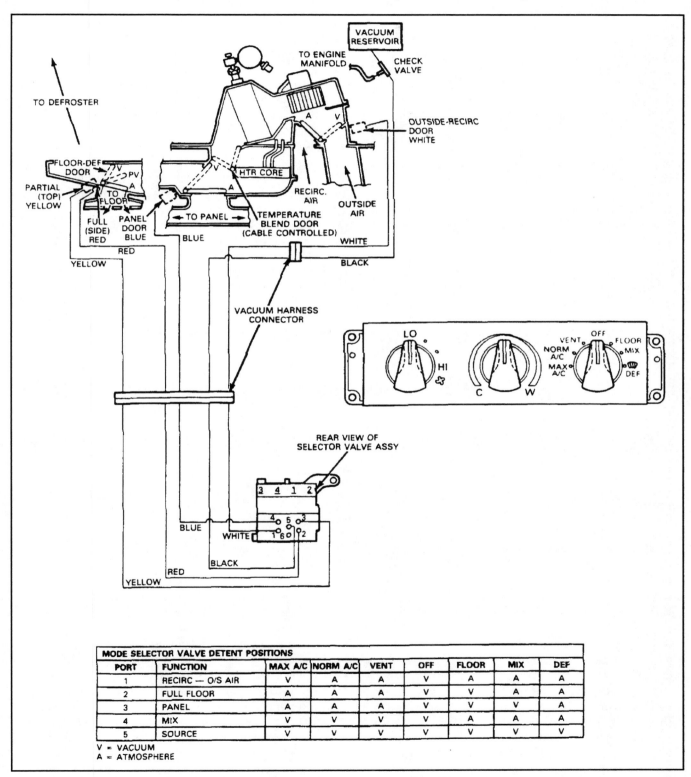

MODE SELECTOR VALVE DETENT POSITIONS								
PORT	FUNCTION	MAX A/C	NORM A/C	VENT	OFF	FLOOR	MIX	DEF
1	RECIRC — O/S AIR	V	A	A	V	A	A	A
2	FULL FLOOR	A	A	A	V	V	A	A
3	PANEL	A	A	A	V	V	V	A
4	MIX	V	V	V	V	A	A	A
5	SOURCE	V	V	V	V	V	V	V

V = VACUUM
A = ATMOSPHERE

A vacuum diagram like this is necessary to diagnose vacuum control problems. (Courtesy: Ford Motor Co.)

head levers, a good system vacuum diagram is necessary.

First, check the system for proper operation. Under all driving conditions, air should come from the appropriate vents when the corresponding mode is selected. If a problem is detected, use the system vacuum diagram to check vacuum flow.

Check the vacuum reservoir check valve to see if it holds vacuum in one direction. Inspect all interior vacuum lines, especially the multi-connection behind the instrument panel. Check the control head for leaky ports or damage, and check all actuators for the ability to hold vacuum.

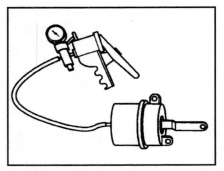

Testing a vacuum operated actuator. *(Courtesy: Ford Motor Co.)*

Finally, disconnect the vacuum line from the actuator and attach a hand-held vacuum pump. Apply vacuum to the actuator. The actuator lever should move to its engaged position and remain there while vacuum is applied. When vacuum is released, the actuator lever should move back to its normal position. Make sure the lever operates smoothly without binding.

To replace the actuator, remove the vacuum line(s) and linkage. Remove the actuator fasteners and the actuator from the vehicle. Reinstall the replacement actuator and fasteners, and reconnect the vacuum lines and linkage. Check for proper operation.

Ducts, Doors And Outlets

Air entering the plenum is directed to whatever vent is selected by a series of ducts underneath the dash. When the desired selection is made at the HVAC control panel, actuators either close or open doors to route the air in the desired direction.

It is important to inspect the plenum doors to make sure they are opening and closing properly. Check the door hinges and actuator connections to make sure they are not binding. Check the adjustment (if equipped) of the actuator arm to make sure all doors are opening fully and closing tightly. Remember, improperly routed air can result in ineffective heating, cooling and defrosting. In addition, unwanted outside air can enter the passenger compartment when inside air is desired, or vice-versa if the ducts and doors are not operating properly.

AUTOMATIC AND SEMI-AUTOMATIC HEATING, VENTILATING AND A/C SYSTEMS

The main difference between manual HVAC and Automatic Temperature Control (ATC) systems is the more precise control of air temperature and routing provided by the ATC system. With automatic controls, the motorist can choose a given temperature, and have this temperature setting maintained by the A/C and heater control system. Sensors determine the present temperature and the system uses actuators to move the air doors to the positions necessary to achieve the desired temperature.

Some newer ATC systems incorporate a feature known as Dual Zone, in which the driver and front passenger can select different temperatures for individual comfort. These work exactly the same way as conventional systems, the only difference being an additional temperature control for the passenger, some additional components inside the plenum, and possibly an additional sun load sensor.

There are two kinds of ATC systems, Semi-Automatic Temperature Control (SATC) and Electronic Automatic Temperature Control (EATC). Semi-automatic systems usually control only the outlet air temperature. In this type of system, the driver still must select the mode of operation and blower speed. As in manual A/C, a switch in the control panel is usually activated to turn on the compressor when the system is placed into the A/C mode, and the water control valve is opened in any mode in which heat may be desired.

EATC systems usually control most of the specific functions of mode of operation, temperature control, blower speeds and, if equipped, water valve action. The system will automatically maintain the desired air temperature and quantity for each mode, and will route the air according to driver selection. In addition, EATC systems have self-diagnostic capabilities.

SATC Systems

SATC system components include the control panel, the programmer and various sensors and actuators. All SATC systems do not have all of the components described here.

The instrument panel mounted control panel is the interface between the driver and the system. The driver selects the desired temperature, the operating mode and the fan speed. The programmer receives the input from the control panel and the system sensors, and in turn controls the blower speed, the air

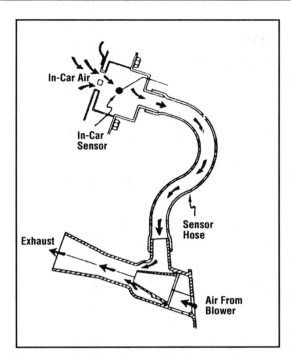

Some manufacturers call the in-car temperature sensor an aspirator. Through the use of a venturi cone in the blower pressure-side air flow, the interior air is drawn through the sensor body.

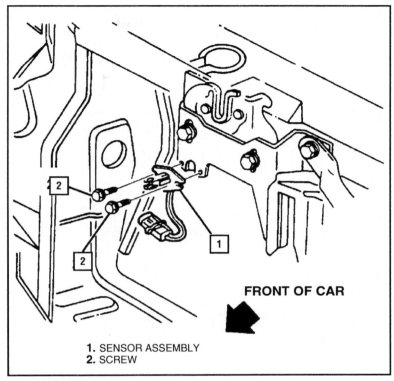

1. SENSOR ASSEMBLY
2. SCREW

Typical ambient temperature sensor mounting location. *(Courtesy: GM Corp.)*

door actuators, the compressor clutch and the heater water valve.

The input sensors include the in-vehicle temperature sensor, the ambient sensor, the sunload sensor and the evaporator temperature sensor. The in-vehicle temperature sensor is an NTC (Negative Temperature Coefficient) thermistor that measures the temperature inside the vehicle. It is located in the aspirator, which is located in the dashboard. The aspirator tube is connected to a heater-A/C duct. The air flowing in the duct past the tube creates a vacuum, drawing in-vehicle air past the sensor. The change in voltage drop across the sensor, as the sensor resistance changes in response to the in-vehicle air temperature, is sent to the programmer.

The ambient temperature sensor is used to measure the temperature of the air outside the

vehicle. It is also an NTC thermistor and functions similarly to the in-vehicle temperature sensor. The ambient temperature sensor is usually located in the front of the vehicle, behind the grill.

The sunload sensor is a photo-voltaic diode that is usually mounted on the top of the dashboard, sometime in a speaker grill. Varying amounts of sunlight striking it modify its electrical return signal to the programmer. Bright sunlight will cause the programmer to adjust system output toward cooler; less sunlight will cause the programmer to adjust system output toward warmer. Some dual zone climate control systems have driver and passenger side sunload sensors.

The evaporator temperature sensor is mounted in the plenum and may have a pickup directly

attached to the evaporator fins. The evaporator temperature sensor is usually an NTC thermistor.

The outputs from the programmer include the air door actuators, compressor clutch control and the heater water valve. The air door actuators can be electric or vacuum motors. The blend door actuator controls the position of the blend door so that the temperature in the vehicle selected by the driver can be maintained. For example, if a cooler temperature is desired, the programmer will move the blend door to partially or completely block air flow through the heater core. If a warmer temperature is desired, the programmer will move the blend door to partially or completely block air flow through the evaporator.

The mode door actuator controls the position of the mode

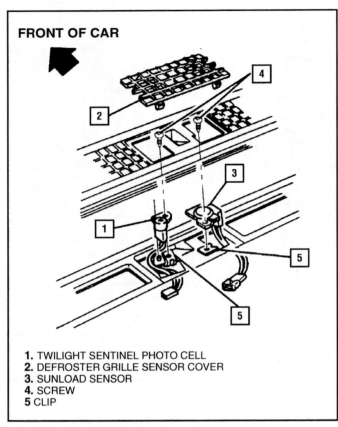

FRONT OF CAR

1. TWILIGHT SENTINEL PHOTO CELL
2. DEFROSTER GRILLE SENSOR COVER
3. SUNLOAD SENSOR
4. SCREW
5 CLIP

Typical sun load sensor mounting location.
(Courtesy: GM Corp.)

door. The programmer, in response to the driver's input, moves the mode door to the position necessary to supply air flow to the desired outlets: the floor ducts, panel ducts or defrost ducts. Some systems have a mix mode, where air flow can be supplied to two ducts, such as when heat and defrost is desired. Some systems will also automatically set air flow to the panel ducts when A/C is selected.

The air inlet door actuator controls the air inlet door so that outside air can be blocked off from inside the vehicle, if desired. When 'MAX A/C' or 'RECIRC' is selected, the programmer will move the air inlet door to block air from outside the vehicle, in order to provide faster cooling.

When 'MAX A/C' is desired, the programmer in some systems will also move the actuator that controls the heater water valve to close, blocking the flow of hot coolant into the heater core.

EATC Systems

The programmer in EATC systems is computer controlled. Control is either through a BCM (Body Control Module) or a computer dedicated to the climate control system. In addition to the computer, a control panel, programmer and the sensors described in the SATC system, EATC systems may also use inputs from the engine coolant temperature sensor, vehicle speed sensor and throttle position sensor.

The door actuators in EATC systems also have potentiometers attached to them. These provide feedback to the computer so the computer knows the exact door position. The resistance in the potentiometer changes according to door position, and the computer reads the voltage drop across the potentiometer.

The BCM, or climate control computer monitors driver and sensor input and uses the information to calculate air door position, blower speed and compressor control. The computer then commands the programmer to operate the actuators.

The BCM, or climate control computer, also monitors the input and feedback signals and compares them to pre-programmed information. If any signals are found to be outside of expected parameters, the computer will store the information in the form of a DTC (Diagnostic Trouble Code) in its memory, and will turn on a light on the instrument panel to alert the driver that service is needed.

System Diagnosis

Troubleshooting automatic temperature control systems is a lot like troubleshooting manual systems. In each case most failures are vacuum or mechanical in nature. Always start by checking the less complicated items first, just as if the vehicle had a manual A/C system. Inspect the air or vacuum supply in addition to the lines and hoses. It is possible that the problem could be caused by leaks in lines, fittings and unions.

Start with a system performance check as on a manual system, but as there are differences in how many of these systems operate, obtain the manufacturer's service information. Use a heat gun to warm the in-vehicle and ambient temperature sensors and see if the system responds with cooler air out of the dash outlets and increased blower speeds. Next, chill the air flow to the sensors to produce the opposite effect; heat from the lower floor vent, and high blower speeds. (Aerosol chilling agents are available at many electronic supply stores.) Place a light source over the sunload sensor to see if the system responds with cooler air output.

If the system reacts with a change to one or two inputs but not to the third, the problem is most likely confined to the single sensor or its circuit. But if no

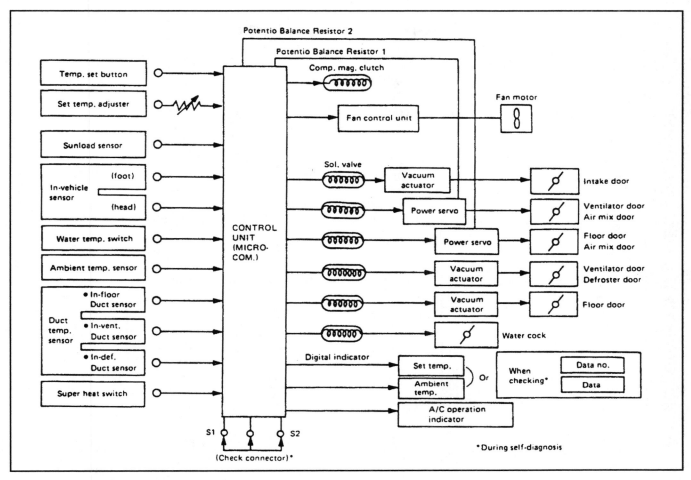

Electrical schematic of an ATC system.

reaction is observed on any of the units, or only a partial reaction is seen, the problem is usually with the programmer or its output units.

Have a helper repeat the tests while you observe components such as vacuum or electric motors throughout the system for movement. If the programmer is good, some movement should occur in response to at least one of the three sensor inputs or the instrument panel controls, since it is unlikely that all of the circuits will simultaneously go bad.

By carefully analyzing the results of sensor and instrument panel control tests, you should be able to pinpoint a problem area.

Many EATC systems require scan tools for in-depth diagnosis, but many provide a method to output fault information on their instrument panel displays, often represented by numerical codes.

The proper function of the EATC system depends upon the electrical inputs of the sensors. The programming that enables the computer to provide control of the system naturally tells the computer how to interpret these signals. To help the technician find trouble, the computer is instructed to know the difference between a reasonable sensor input and one that indicates the sensor is not functioning properly.

Should the system begin to operate erratically, the computer will record that fact and store a DTC that will tell the technician what has happened. The goal of this system is not only to lead the technician in the right direction, but also to retain information about a fault that might be intermittent and may not be evident when the vehicle is brought in for service.

If the control panel has a digital display, the temperature indication on the display would be replaced by the failure code number when in the diagnostic mode. Start the engine and let it warm up to operating temperature. Following the manufacturer's instructions, activate the digital display to read the diagnostic codes. Record all codes displayed during the test. If error codes appear during the test, follow the diagnostic procedures outlined by the manufacturer.

If the control panel does not have a digital display, connect a suitable scan tool to the diagnostic data link and read active or stored DTCs. Compare these codes with the manufacturer's trouble code list to pinpoint the problem.

Most temperature sensors can be tested for resistance and voltage drop. Refer to the vehicle service information for specifications and testing procedures. In general, the sensor should be replaced if its resistance is not within specification. If resistance is infinite, check for an open circuit in the wiring upstream of the sensor. Since a temperature sensor's resistance varies with temperature, check the sensor voltage against temperature and compare to manufacturer's specifications.

Aspirator Testing

If air is not drawn past the in-vehicle temperature sensor, the sensor will not be able to accurately measure the temperature inside the vehicle. To check aspirator function, place the blower on high and the function mode on heat. Place a small piece of paper over the aspirator inlet or place a lighted cigarette in front of the aspirator inlet. The paper should be held against the aspirator inlet due to suction or the smoke from the cigarette should be sucked into the aspirator.

If the aspirator does not func-

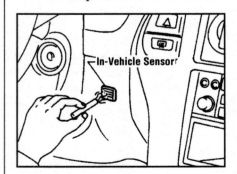

Aspirator testing.
(Courtesy: Nissan Motor Co., Ltd.)

tion as indicated, check for an obstruction in the duct or aspirator tube or for a loose connection.

In-Vehicle And Ambient Temperature Sensor Testing

Disconnect the sensor harness connector. Connect the leads of a DMM in the ohms position to the sensor terminals. Heat or cool the sensor as necessary and compare the resistance with manufacturer's specifications. Replace the sensor if it is not within specifications.

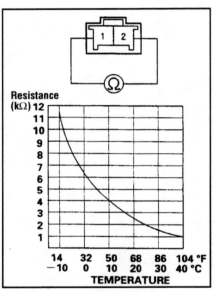

An example of resistance specifications for an in-vehicle temperature sensor.
(Courtesy: Honda Motor Co., Ltd.)

Sunload Sensor Testing

Remove the sensor from the

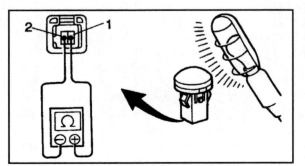

Sunload sensor testing.
(Courtesy: Toyota Motor Corp.)

vehicle. Connect the leads of a DMM in the ohms position to the sensor terminals. Cover the sensor with a cloth and check that no continuity exists between the terminals. If continuity exists, replace the sensor.

Remove the cloth and place a light over the sensor. Continuity should now exist between the terminals. If no continuity exists, replace the sensor.

Evaporator Temperature Sensor Testing

Remove the evaporator temperature sensor from the vehicle. Place the sensor and a thermometer in a container of cold water. Connect the leads of a DMM in the ohms position to the sensor terminals. Gradually heat the water, noting the change in temperature and resistance.

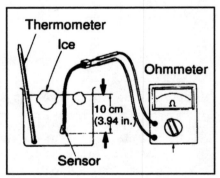

Evaporator temperature sensor testing.
(Courtesy: Toyota Motor Co.)

Compare the resistance/temperature readings with manufacturer's specifications and replace the sensor as necessary.

NOTES

REFRIGERANT RECOVERY, RECYCLING, HANDLING AND RETROFIT

Studies indicate that CFCs (R12 is one) are depleting the earth's protective ozone layer located in the stratosphere. This precious layer, some 10 to 30 miles above the planet's surface, filters out most of the sun's harmful ultraviolet rays.

Section 609 of the Clean Air Act of 1990 states that automotive air conditioning technicians are required to recover and recycle all refrigerant using a machine designed and approved to do the job. All A/C technicians must be certified to do so.

EQUIPMENT

According to the Clean Air Act, all equipment used for the recovery and recycling of refrigerant must meet J1990 specs, which provide equipment specifications for hardware related issues. Hoses must have shutoff valves within 12-in. of their ends. Filters must be able to trap particles as small as 15 microns in diameter. The equipment must be able to measure, in 1 oz. units, how much oil has been drawn from the A/C system.

The equipment must be able to extract and process the refrigerant to purity levels spelled out in the J1991 companion document. It specifies a limit, in parts per million (ppm) by weight, for three different contaminants:
• Moisture (15 ppm),
• Refrigerant oil (4000 ppm)
• Non condensable gases (air) (330 ppm).

Recovery/recycling equipment approved by Underwriters Laboratories (UL) is capable of cleaning refrigerant to the J1991 purity standard. The equipment you use must be UL approved and certified to meet J1991 standards. Recovery/recycling equip-

ment both recovers the refrigerant from the motor vehicle and processes it through an oil separator, a filter, and a dryer.

Recover-only equipment removes the refrigerant from the A/C unit and transfers it into a holding tank. Technicians are then required by law either to recycle the used refrigerant on site or send it to an off-site reclamation facility to be purified.

The two styles of recovery/recycling equipment: single-pass and multi-pass, draw the refrigerant from the A/C system, filters and separates the oil, removes moisture and air, and stores the refrigerant until it's ready to be reused. The refrigerant goes through each stage before being stored and ready for reuse in single-pass systems. It may go through all or some of the stages before being stored in multi-pass systems.

REFRIGERANT IDENTIFICATION

Refrigerant contamination levels in excess of 5 percent can result in pressure control problems, air quality and flow problems, and valve blockage. In addition, resulting hose and seal degradation can contaminate the system further, causing more expensive repairs than anticipated.

Checking refrigerant pressures does not guarantee that you will recognize that refrigerant is contaminated or is a brand that is unfamiliar to you. However, refrigerant identification tools can help you. The identifier can confirm the chemical composition of refrigerant, and sometimes indicate flammable substances and air content.

Be aware that different refrigerant mixtures can result in a

mixture that is not recognized by the identifier because the original intent was to identify R12 and R134a refrigerants. Because other refrigerants are now available, identification problems are now more complex. Service facilities should establish how these identifiers respond to different refrigerant mixtures and contamination.

Depending on the manufacturer, the identifier can be a hand-held tool, which will identify whether the refrigerant is pure R12 or R134a, or be part of a complete refrigerant recovery/recycling station, which can aid in complete A/C diagnostics. Always follow the identifier manufacturer's instructions when using this type of equipment.

RECOVERING REFRIGERANT

You must keep the discharge of refrigerant to a minimum when recovering refrigerant. All A/C service hoses must have shutoff valves within 12-in. (30cm) of the service ends: manual shutoff valves or Schrader valves, or quick disconnect fittings with automatic shutoff. The purpose of shutoff valves is to minimize the amount of CFCs that escape into the atmosphere. Shutoff valves also minimize the amount of air that may enter the recycling equipment.

Always follow the equipment manufacturer's instructions. Recover the refrigerant from the vehicle and continue the process until the equipment gauges show a vacuum in the system. Turn off the recovery/recycling unit, but leave it connected to the vehicle for at least five minutes to see if the system has any residual pressure. If so, repeat the process to remove any remaining refrigerant until the A/C system holds a stable vacuum for at least five minutes.

Systems with accumulators usually require some extra time for recovery because accumulators can get very cold and refrigerant can become dissolved in the lubricant retained by the accumulator. Some refrigerant may remain in the accumulator and be released as it warms up. Make sure you remove all refrigerant before disconnecting any of the system's components.

Before disconnecting the equipment, close the valves in the service hoses. You may now make any necessary repairs to the A/C system.

RECYCLING

In general, properly recycled refrigerant can be removed from the vehicle's air conditioner, recycled on site, and then charged into the same or a different vehicle. Recycled refrigerant is identified as refrigerant that has been recovered from an A/C system and cleaned in accordance with SAE standards. The equipment is only designed to remove contaminants that are normally picked up during A/C operation. Recycling equipment meeting SAE standards for refrigerant must be labeled according to the specific refrigerant it is designed to recycle.

According to the EPA, once recovered, refrigerant should not be recycled on-site unless it is uncontaminated R12 or R134a. Recovering contaminated R12 or R134a refrigerant into recycling equipment may damage the equipment. In addition, the EPA regulations currently prohibit technicians from recycling blend substitute refrigerants (contaminated or not). EPA is working with independent testing laboratories and with equipment manu-

facturers, to determine whether it is possible to develop recycling equipment to service these blends, which would protect both the health and safety of the technician and the integrity of the A/C system.

STORING AND DISPOSAL

It is illegal to use anything but 'DOT CFR Title 49' containers for recycled refrigerant. Markings '4BA' or '4BW' on the side show that it meets DOT CFR Title 49 requirements. Never collect, salvage or store refrigerant in a disposable container.

Evacuate the container to at least 27-in. Hg vacuum (75mm Hg absolute pressure) before transferring the refrigerant. To prevent overfilling during transfer of refrigerant, never fill a container to more than 60 percent of its gross weight rating. If the refrigerant is contaminated beyond the point where it can be cleaned, the contents should be recovered to be reclaimed by an EPA-certified refrigerant reclaimer.

Containers still have traces of refrigerant in them even though they may appear to be empty. Evacuate all remaining refrigerant using your recovery/recycling apparatus before disposing of the container. To remove any remaining refrigerant, connect your recovery/recycling unit to the container and recover the refrigerant. Once the container shows a vacuum, close its valve. Write the word 'EMPTY' on the container and dispose of it in accordance with all applicable laws.

TESTING FOR NON-CONDENSABLE GASES

Before using recycled refrigerant, you must check it for excess non-condensable gases (air). After storing the container at 65°F (18°C) or above for 12 hours out of

direct sunlight, connect a gauge, calibrated in 1-psi divisions, to the container and read the pressure. Also check the air temperature within 4-in. of the container with an accurate thermometer. Compare your pressure reading to a standard temperature-pressure chart. Be sure the pressure is at, or below, the limits shown for a given temperature.

The refrigerant can be used as is if the pressure of the recycled refrigerant is lower than the limit shown for a given temperature. If the pressure is higher than the limit shown for a given temperature, there is air in the tank. To purge the air, connect the tank to the recovery/recycling machine and slowly vent the air vapor from the top of the container. Continue venting until the pressure falls below the limit shown on your chart. If the pressure inside the container still exceeds the pressure limit shown, recycle the entire contents.

RETROFITTING

As long as R12 refrigerant is available, a properly functioning R12 system should be serviced with R12 refrigerant. Retrofitting should only be done if the system is malfunctioning and needs repair.

The expense and amount of work required to change an R12 system over to R134a depends on the age of the vehicle and the condition of the system components. Late model R12 system vehicles should require less time and money, since many of the last R12 vehicles built were equipped with barrier type hoses, which are necessary for R134a refrigerant, and many were equipped with compressors and receiver/driers or accumulators that are R134a compatible. Older vehicles will probably cost more and require more work, since many of their components will be worn and incompatible with R134a refrigerant.

Both the aftermarket and the vehicle manufacturers produce kits that include everything needed to retrofit. Depending on the vehicle, a kit includes:

• Replacement hoses
• R134a service fittings
• Replacement O-rings
• Replacement orifice tube or TXV calibrated for R134a
• Replacement switches calibrated for R134a
• High-pressure cutoff switch
• Replacement accumulator or receiver/drier with XH-7 or XH-9 desiccant
• PAG or ester oil
• An R134a identification label indicating retrofit information.

Before beginning the retrofit procedure, inspect the existing A/C system and do a performance test, to find out if any repairs are required.

Properly recover the R12 refrigerant from the system. During recovery, at least 99 percent of the R12 must be removed from the system and as much of the mineral oil as possible. This is important because the oil has absorbed R12 and even a small percentage of R12 left in the system will cause excessive high side pressure. The oil can be drained or flushed out, but on some vehicles component removal may be required to remove all of the refrigerant oil.

Perform any repairs as indicated by the system inspection and performance test. If there was a compressor failure, flush the system and install a filter in the high side, then install the new compressor. Install a new receiver/drier or accumulator.

If the system does not have a high-pressure relief valve, install a high-pressure cutoff switch. This switch senses high side pressure and is connected to the compressor clutch or relay in order to interrupt compressor operation. Install any other switches and valves supplied with the kit.

Install the replacement hoses using the new O-rings supplied with the kit. Also replace the O-rings on any connections that were not disturbed, as required. Add the proper amount of PAG or ester oil to the compressor inlet.

Install the R134a service fittings. These are usually conversion fittings that are installed on the existing R12 fittings. If the R12 fittings are not converted, they must be permanently capped.

Install the retrofit label over the existing R12 reference label. If the R134a label is not installed over the R12 label, the R12 label must be rendered unreadable. The new label must list the name and address of the company or person that performed the retrofit, the date of the retrofit and the type and amount of refrigerant and lubricant in the system.

Evacuate the system for at least 30 minutes with a minimum vacuum of 25-in. Hg. Charge the system with R134a refrigerant, keeping in mind that the system will only require 80-90 percent of the original R12 charge amount. Check the system for leaks and proper performance.

CERTIFICATION FOR HANDLING REFRIGERANT

Many organizations now provide the certification called for in the Clean Air Act, but such certification should not be confused with the regular ASE Heating and Air Conditioning Technician Certification Test A7.

Except in selected locales, the refrigerant recovery and recycling tests are open-book exams designed to acquaint the technician with the environmental issues, as well as proper techniques for handling CFCs. Once the test is passed, the technician will receive a certificate, which will entitle him or her to purchase CFCs, and also legally work on automotive refrigeration systems.

Organizations that provide certification include the following:

ASE Refrigerant Recovery and Recycling Review and Quiz
101 Blue Seal Drive
Suite 101
Leesburg, VA 20175
Phone 703-669-6600
http://www.asecert.org

International Mobile Air Conditioning Association (IMACA)
P.O. Box 9000
Fort Worth, TX 76147-2000
Phone 817-338-1100
Fax 817-338-1451
http://www.imaca.org

Mobile Air Conditioning Society (MACS)
P.O. Box 100
East Greenville, PA 18041
Phone 215-541-4500
Fax 215-679-4977
http://www.macsw.org

In addition to these certification organizations, the following is a list of programs, obtained from the EPA, offering air conditioning exams and credentials. You can check out the latest list at the EPA Web site. This list will be updated when other technician certification programs are approved.

An asterisk (*) indicates that the program offers home study.

A double asterisk (**) indicates that the program offers training and testing on the Internet. Where available, addresses (URLs) have been provided to web sites.

Air Conditioning Contractors of
America/Ferris State University*
1712 New Hampshire Avenue, NW
Washington, DC 20009
Phone: 202-483-9370
http://www.acca.org

C.F.C. Reclamation and Recycling
Service, Inc.
P.O. Box 560
Abilene, TX 79604
Phone: 915- 675-5311
http://www.c-f-c.com

ESCO Institute*
1350 West Northwest Highway,
Suite 205
Mount Prospect, IL 60056
Phone: 800-726-9696
http://www.escoinst.com

The Greater Cleveland
Automobile Dealers' Association*
6100 Rockside Woods Boulevard,
Suite 235
Independence, OH 44131
Phone: 216-328-1500
http://www.gcada.org

Mainstream Engineering Corp.**
200 Yellow Place
Rockledge, FL 32955
Phone: 407-631-3550
http://www.epatest.com

Mechanic's Education Association
1805 Springfield Avenue
Maple Shade, New Jersey 07040
Phone: 973-426-9001
http://www.iatn.net/atn/techline.html

New York State Association of
Service Stations and Repair
Shops, Inc.
Automotive Technician Training
Program
12 Walker Way
Albany, NY 12207
Phone: 518-452-4367
http://www.albany.net/~gra

New York State Department of
Motor Vehicles, Division of
Vehicle Safety
Technical Training Unit
Empire State Plaza
Swan Street Building, Room 111
Albany, NY 12228
Phone: 518-474-4049

Rancho Santiago College
1530 West 17th
Santa Ana, CA 92706
Phone: 714-564-6661
http://www.rancho.cc.ca.us

Snap-on Tools Corporation
2801 80th Street
Kenosha, WI 53141-1410
Phone: 414-656-5200
http://www.snapon.com

Texas Engineering Extension
Service
San Antonio Training Division
The Texas A&M University
System
9350 South Presa
San Antonio, TX 78223-4799
Phone: 512-633-1000

Waco Chemicals, Inc.*
12306 Montague Street
Pacoima, CA 91331
Phone: 818-897-3018

Universal Technical Institute*
3002 North 27th Avenue
Phoenix, AZ 85017
Phone: 800-859-7249
http://www.uticorp.com/index.html

Vatterott College
10265 St. Charles Rock Road
St. Louis, MO 63074
Phone: 314-843-4200
http://www.vatterott-college.com/home

For information on EPA regulations, assistance on regulatory
compliance or to express your
opinion, you may also contact the
EPA Small Business Ombudsman
at 800-368-5888.

NOTES

NOTES

Prepare yourself for ASE testing with these questions on
HEATING AND AIR CONDITIONING

NOTE: The following questions are written in the ASE style. They are similar to the kinds of questions that you will see on the ASE test, however none of these questions will actually appear on the test.

1. Technician A says that evacuating an A/C system will remove air and moisture from the system. Technician B says that evacuating an A/C system will remove dirt particles from the system. Who is right?

    A. Technician A only
    B. Technician B only
    C. Both A and B
    D. Neither A or B

2. There is a growling or rumbling noise at the A/C compressor when the system is off and the engine is running. The noise stops when the system is turned on. Technician A says that a bad compressor bearing could be the cause. Technician B says that a bad compressor clutch bearing could be the cause. Who is right?

    A. Technician A only
    B. Technician B only
    C. Both A and B
    D. Neither A or B

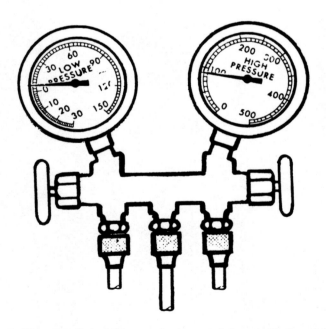

3. The readings shown above are taken with the A/C system operating at an ambient (outside) temperature of 85°F (29°C). What do the readings indicate?

    A. normal operation
    B. low refrigerant level
    C. a restriction in the high side
    D. damaged compressor

4. Recovery/recycling equipment must have shutoff valves located within 12-in. (30 cm) of the hoses' service ends so that:

    A. oil can be added to the refrigerant
    B. the unit can be isolated from the refrigerant source
    C. the filter can be changed without disconnecting the hoses
    D. refrigerant discharge can be kept to a minimum

5. When recovering refrigerant from an A/C system, how long should the technician wait after the recovery/recycling unit has been turned off to see if there is any residual pressure in the system?

    A. 1 minute
    B. 5 minutes
    C. 10 minutes
    D. 15 minutes

6. A system with a low pressure on the low side and a heavy frost accumulation on the inlet side of the Thermostatic Expansion Valve (TXV) indicates a:

    A. TXV stuck open
    B. clogged condenser
    C. defective compressor
    D. clogged screen or TXV stuck closed

7. A blower motor only works on high speed. Which of the following causes is the **MOST** likely?

    A. defective blower relay
    B. defective blower resistor
    C. defective blower switch
    D. blown fuse or tripped circuit breaker

8. A customer complains that when accelerating his car with the A/C on, the cold air flow from the dash outlets shifts to the floor. Technician A says that this is caused by a faulty check valve in the vacuum reservoir. Technician B says that this condition is due to a vacuum leak. Who is right?

    A. Technician A only
    B. Technician B only
    C. Both A and B
    D. Neither A or B

9. When pressure testing the cooling system on a late model gasoline engine vehicle, the pressure on the tester drops but no leaks can be found in the engine compartment. Technician A starts the engine and, seeing the pressure on the tester gauge increase, says that there is an internal leak, a blown head gasket. Technician B says that there cannot be an internal leak because the engine oil looks normal, not milky like it would be if coolant were present, and there is no white smoke coming from the exhaust pipe. Who is right?

    A. Technician A only
    B. Technician B only
    C. Both A and B
    D. Neither A or B

10. When identifying an A/C system, Technician A says that an accumulator located between the evaporator and compressor is an indication that the system has an orifice tube. Technician B says that when the high side service port fitting is smaller than the one on the low side, the system uses R134a refrigerant. Who is right?

    A. Technician A only
    B. Technician B only
    C. Both A and B
    D. Neither A or B

11. When troubleshooting an ATC system, the system responds when the ambient and in-vehicle temperature sensors are heated and cooled. However, there is no response when the sunload sensor is exposed to a light source. Technician A says that the problem is with the system's programmer. Technician B says that the problem is with the sunload sensor. Who is right?

    A. Technician A only
    B. Technician B only
    C. Both A and B
    D. Neither A or B

12. The following are all methods of orifice tube replacement EXCEPT:

    A. Replace the line that incorporates the orifice tube.
    B. Disconnect the liquid line from the evaporator inlet line and pull the orifice tube straight out with an extractor tool.
    C. Disconnect the liquid line from the evaporator inlet line and, using a twisting motion to break free of the line, pull out the orifice tube with an extractor tool.
    D. Cut out the section of line that contains the orifice tube and, using a kit, install a new orifice tube line segment.

13. When converting the A/C system in an older vehicle to R134a refrigerant, what percentage of the original R12 charge amount should be used?

    A. 75 percent
    B. 100 percent
    C. 99 percent
    D. 80-90 percent

14. A vehicle with R134a refrigerant in the A/C system has a refrigerant leak. Technician A says that a propane gas leak detector should be used to find the location of the leak. Technician B says that an electronic leak detector should be used to check for leaks. Who is right?

    A. Technician A only
    B. Technician B only
    C. Both A and B
    D. Neither A or B

15. Which of the following is a true statement regarding R134a refrigerant?

    A. It is harmful to the ozone layer.
    B. It mixes with mineral oil.
    C. It requires a different desiccant than R12.
    D. It operates at lower pressures than R12.

16. The compressor in an A/C system does not run. When a jumper wire is used to connect the battery positive terminal to the power connector, the compressor clutch engages. Technician A says that the clutch coil is defective. Technician B says that the pressure cycling switch could be defective. Who is right?

    A. Technician A only
    B. Technician B only
    C. Both A and B
    D. Neither A or B

17. The floor inside a vehicle is wet and there is a slimy film on the windows. Technician A says that the heater core is leaking. Technician B says that the evaporator case drain plug is clogged. Who is right?

    A. Technician A only
    B. Technician B only
    C. Both A and B
    D. Neither A or B

Prepare yourself for ASE testing with these questions on HEATING AND AIR CONDITIONING

18. During A/C system operation, a knocking sound can be heard coming from the compressor. Technician A says that there could be internal compressor damage. Technician B says that the compressor mounting brackets and bushings should be checked. Who is right?
    A. Technician A only
    B. Technician B only
    C. Both A and B
    D. Neither A or B

19. All of the following could cause poor heater performance **EXCEPT**:
    A. defective temperature blend door actuator
    B. radiator coolant temperature below 150°F (66°C)
    C. heater core return hose much cooler than inlet hose
    D. stuck open heater control valve

20. During an A/C system performance test, the air temperature at the center outlet duct is warm to slightly cool and the low and high side pressures on the manifold gauge set are both low. All of the following could be the cause of these symptoms **EXCEPT**:
    A. clogged orifice tube
    B. expansion valve stuck closed
    C. restricted receiver/drier
    D. plugged condenser

21. What is the minimum system pressure necessary to leak test with an electronic leak detector?
    A. 25 psi
    B. 50 psi
    C. 75 psi
    D. 100 psi

22. Technician A says that when retrofitting an A/C system, the new R134a service ports are usually installed on the existing R12 fittings. Technician B says that if the old fittings are not converted, they should be labeled. Who is right?
    A. Technician A only
    B. Technician B only
    C. Both A and B
    D. Neither A or B

23. When diagnosing an ATC system, most of the system temperature sensors can be tested for:
    A. resistance and current flow
    B. resistance and voltage drop
    C. voltage drop and current flow
    D. current flow and continuity

24. During an A/C system performance test, high side pressure was found to be excessive and the A/C compressor continued to run. Technician A says that the high-pressure cutout switch could be defective. Technician B says that there could be an air flow obstruction at the condenser. Who is right?
    A. Technician A only
    B. Technician B only
    C. Both A and B
    D. Neither A or B

25. The A/C compressor cycles rapidly, and air coming from the vents is only slightly cool. Technician A says the problem could be a low refrigerant charge. Technician B says the problem could be a defective thermostatic switch. Who is right?
    A. Technician A only
    B. Technician B only
    C. Both A and B
    D. Neither A or B

26. To properly evacuate an A/C system, the vacuum pump should be operated a minimum of:
    A. 5 minutes
    B. 10 minutes
    C. 20 minutes
    D. 30 minutes

27. Technician A says that a special tool is required to disconnect and connect spring lock fittings. Technician B says that when assembling new spring lock fittings, new O-rings lubricated with clean refrigerant oil should be used. Who is right?
    A. Technician A only
    B. Technician B only
    C. Both A and B
    D. Neither A or B

28. All of the following are true statements concerning in-line filters **EXCEPT**:
   A. They are usually installed in a system that has suffered a compressor failure.
   B. They are installed to protect the new compressor from metal chips or other debris that could be in the system from the original compressor failure.
   C. They are installed to collect debris that could clog the orifice tube or expansion valve filters.
   D. Filters are only installed in the high side of the system.

29. Two technicians are discussing sight glass observations. Technician A says that if foam is seen in the sight glass, the refrigerant charge is low. Technician B says that if oil streaks are seen in the sight glass, the refrigerant charge is low. Who is right?
   A. Technician A only
   B. Technician B only
   C. Both A and B
   D. Neither A or B

30. Technician A says that moisture in an A/C system can freeze in the expansion valve and stop the system from cooling. Technician B says that moisture in the A/C system will react with R12 to form an acid that can cause corrosion. Who is right?
   A. Technician A only
   B. Technician B only
   C. Both A and B
   D. Neither A or B

31. Low heater output can be caused by all of the following **EXCEPT**:
   A. an engine low on coolant
   B. a stuck open cooling system thermostat
   C. a restricted heater control valve
   D. a disengaged clutch type radiator fan

32. The high side pressure in an A/C system is above specifications. All of the following could cause this problem **EXCEPT**:
   A. an overcharge of refrigerant
   B. restricted air flow across the condenser
   C. a slipping fan belt
   D. a broken compressor reed valve

33. When filling a container with recycled refrigerant, to what percentage of the container's gross weight rating should it be filled?
   A. 50 percent
   B. 60 percent
   C. 70 percent
   D. 80 percent

34. A vacuum door actuator is being tested. When vacuum is applied with a hand held vacuum pump, the door does not move and the reading on the vacuum gauge is zero. Technician A says that the door does not move because it is binding or obstructed. Technician B says that the door does not move because the actuator is defective. Who is right?
   A. Technician A only
   B. Technician B only
   C. Both A and B
   D. Neither A or B

35. A customer complains of a foul odor coming from the dash outlets whenever the A/C and blower are on. Technician A says that this is caused by a clogged evaporator drain. Technician B says that this is caused by bacterial growth on the evaporator. Who is right?
   A. Technician A only
   B. Technician B only
   C. Both A and B
   D. Neither A or B

36. When an A/C system is operating, a clicking or buzzing noise is heard coming from the compressor. Technician A says that this noise means that the system is overcharged. Technician B says that the noise could be due to air in the system. Who is right?
   A. Technician A only
   B. Technician B only
   C. Both A and B
   D. Neither A or B

37. A customer complains that when parallel parking, his car repeatedly stalls, but only when the air conditioning is on. Technician A says that the power steering pressure switch is defective. Technician B says that there is a problem with the power steering pump. Who is right?
   A. Technician A only
   B. Technician B only
   C. Both A and B
   D. Neither A or B

Prepare yourself for ASE testing with these questions on
HEATING AND AIR CONDITIONING

38. All of the following are true statements about receiver/driers **EXCEPT**:
   A. They may have a sight glass located on the top.
   B. They store liquid refrigerant.
   C. They keep liquid refrigerant from entering the compressor.
   D. They contain a desiccant to absorb moisture from the system.

39. Technician A says that the pressure cycling switch is usually located on the accumulator. Technician B says that the refrigerant must be recovered from the system before the switch can be removed. Who is right?
   A. Technician A only
   B. Technician B only
   C. Both A and B
   D. Neither A or B

40. Technician A says that the A/C system can be charged through the high or low side only when the engine is not running. Technician B says that the A/C system can be charged though the low side when the engine is running. Who is right?
   A. Technician A only
   B. Technician B only
   C. Both A and B
   D. Neither A or B

41. An air conditioning check has uncovered a discharge in the system and compressor damage. Technician A says that after the repairs are made, to check the low-pressure cutoff switch. Technician B says lubricating oil is carried by the refrigerant through the system. Who is right?
   A. Technician A only
   B. Technician B only
   C. Both A and B
   D. Neither A or B

42. When checking recycled refrigerant for excess non-condensable gases (air), Technician A says that the container must be stored at 65°F (18°C) or above for 8 hours out of direct sunlight, before checking the pressure. Technician B says if the pressure is higher than the limit shown for a given temperature, there is air in the tank. Who is right?
   A. Technician A only
   B. Technician B only
   C. Both A and B
   D. Neither A or B

43. The operation of the thermostatic switch depends on the temperature of the:
   A. condenser
   B. compressor
   C. evaporator
   D. outside air

44. All of the following are causes for fan clutch replacement **EXCEPT**:
   A. oil film on the back of the clutch
   B. no viscous drag
   C. fan speed does not increase as engine warms up
   D. when engine is hot, fan stops spinning in only two seconds after shut down

45. Technician A says that an ambient temperature switch protects the compressor from damage. Technician B says that an ambient temperature sensor provides input for the Automatic Temperature Control (ATC) system. Who is right?
   A. Technician A only
   B. Technician B only
   C. Both A and B
   D. Neither A or B

46. If a capillary tube was to break at some point between its sensing bulb and the expansion valve, what affect would it have on the valve?
   A. The expansion valve would stick open.
   B. The expansion valve would stick closed
   C. The expansion valve would stick in whatever position it was in at the time of the break.
   D. There would be no affect on the expansion valve.

47. A customer has a complaint of poor heat output. After checking the hoses running from the heater core and finding them both to be hot, Technician A says the problem could be a clogged heater core. Technician B says a misadjusted temperature control cable could be the problem. Who is right?
>   A. Technician A only
>   B. Technician B only
>   C. Both A and B
>   D. Neither A or B

48. The R134a retrofit label that is placed over the existing R12 reference label must include all of the following information **EXCEPT**:
>   A. name and address of the company or person that performed the retrofit
>   B. retrofit kit manufacturer's name
>   C. date of the retrofit
>   B. type and amount of refrigerant and lubricant in the system.

49. During the diagnosis of an ATC system, a trouble code is obtained that references the blend door feedback sensor. Technician A says that the sensor should be replaced. Technician B says that the sensor circuit should be tested. Who is right?
>   A. Technician A only
>   B. Technician B only
>   C. Both A and B
>   D. Neither A or B

50. A major cause for the depletion of the ozone layer has been attributed to:
>   A. carbon monoxide (CO) fumes from automotive exhaust
>   B. unburned hydrocarbon (HC) emissions from automobile exhaust
>   C. the release of chlorofluorocarbons (CFCs) into the atmosphere
>   D. all of the above

51. Which of the following sensors is NOT an NTC thermistor?
>   A. in-vehicle sensor
>   B. ambient sensor
>   C. sunload sensor
>   D. engine coolant temperature sensor

Prepare yourself for ASE testing with these questions on
HEATING AND AIR CONDITIONING

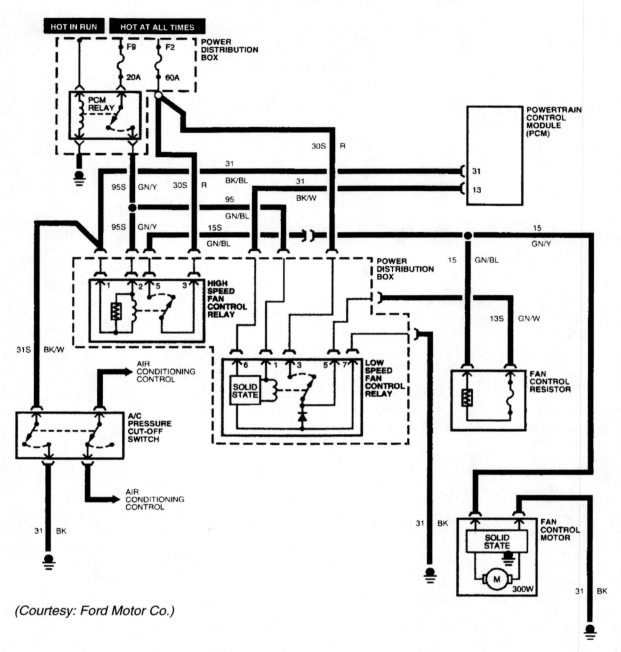

(Courtesy: Ford Motor Co.)

The next two questions refer to the above schematic.

52. The cooling fan works on low speed but not on high speed. Which of the following could be the cause?
    A. a faulty fan control resistor
    B. an open in circuit 95S between the 95/95S splice and the high speed relay
    C. a short to ground in circuit 95S between the 95/95S splice and the high speed relay
    D. blown 60 amp fuse

53. This time the cooling fan works on high speed but not on low speed. All of the following are possible causes **EXCEPT**:
    A. a poor connection at the junction of circuit 13S and the power distribution box
    B. an open in circuit 30S
    C. a faulty fan control resistor
    D. an open in circuit 15 between the 15/15S splice and the fan motor.

54. A customer with an SATC equipped vehicle complains that the car does not get cool enough on hot days. Technician A says that the blend door actuator is probably malfunctioning. Technician B says that the programmer is the problem. Who is right?
A. Technician A only
B. Technician B only
C. Both A and B
D. Neither A or B

55. A compressor clutch will not engage. All of the following could be the cause **EXCEPT**:
A. a closed high-pressure cutout switch
B. low refrigerant level
C. an open ambient temperature switch
D. faulty compressor clutch coil

56. The inside of an EATC equipped vehicle never feels as cool as the temperature setting. The A/C system checks out OK, including the sensors. Technician A says there could be an obstruction in the aspirator tube. Technician B says the aspirator tube could be disconnected from the duct. Who is right?
A. Technician A only
B. Technician B only
C. Both A and B
D. Neither A or B

57. The ambient temperature sensor in an EATC system is being tested. Technician A says that the resistance of the sensor should increase as it is heated. Technician B says that, as the sensor resistance changes, the computer reads the change in voltage drop across the sensor. Who is right?
A. Technician A only
B. Technician B only
C. Both A and B
D. Neither A or B

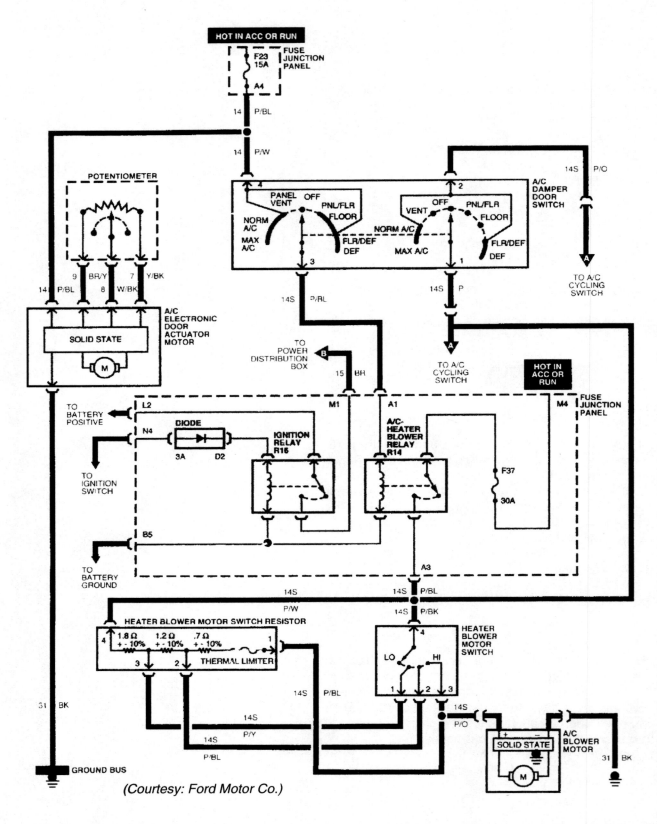

(Courtesy: Ford Motor Co.)

The following three questions refer to the above schematic.

58. The blower motor works on all speeds except low. Technician A says that this could be caused by an open in the 1.8-ohm resistor. Technician B says that this could be caused by an open in circuit 14S between the P/BL and P/O splice and the motor. Who is right?

A. Technician A only
B. Technician B only
C. Both A and B
D. Neither A or B

Prepare yourself for ASE testing with these questions on
HEATING AND AIR CONDITIONING

59. The blower motor only works on high. Which of the following could be the cause?
       A. an open thermal limiter
       B. a blown 30 amp fuse
       C. an open in circuit 31
       D. an open in the P/BK wire between the P/B2 and P/BK splice and the blower switch

60. When the A/C damper door switch is placed in the MAX A/C position, the compressor clutch does not engage. However, a test light illuminates when placed at pin 1 of the A/C damper door switch. Which of the following could be the cause?
       A. An open in the P/BL wire of circuit 14S
       B. A faulty A/C damper door switch
       C. A blown 30 amp fuse
       D. A faulty A/C heater blower relay

NOTES

NOTES

Answers to Study-Guide Test Questions

1. The correct answer is A. Evacuating an A/C system removes air and moisture from the system. The receiver/drier may contain a filter or strainer to catch and trap foreign particles and dirt, but this remains in the receiver/drier and is not removed during the evacuation procedure.

2. The correct answer is B. The compressor clutch bearing allows the rotor/pulley assembly to spin independently of the compressor shaft when the A/C system is off. When the engine is running and the A/C system is off, the compressor clutch bearing is spinning. When the A/C system is turned on, the rotor/pulley assembly and the armature are locked together by the magnetic action of the compressor clutch coil.

3. The correct answer is B. Low pressure on both the low side and the high side indicates a low refrigerant charge.

4. The correct answer is D. According to the Clean Air Act, recovery/recycling equipment must have shutoff valves located within 12-in. (30 cm) of the hoses' service ends so that refrigerant discharge to the atmosphere can be kept to a minimum.

5. The correct answer is B. The technician should wait five minutes and watch the gauges to see if there is any residual pressure. If there is, repeat the process to remove any remaining refrigerant until the A/C system holds a stable vacuum for at least five minutes.

6. The correct answer is D. A low pressure reading on the low side and a heavy frost accumulation on the inlet side of the TXV indicates a clogged screen at the expansion valve inlet or a TXV stuck closed.

7. The correct answer is B. Answer D is incorrect because if the blower fuse was blown or circuit breaker tripped, the blower would not work at all. Answer A is incorrect because a blower relay is generally only used for the high blower speed and this is working. Answer C, the blower switch is a possible cause but the most likely cause for operation on only high speed is that a portion of the resistor assembly is burned out.

8. The correct answer is C, both technicians. If, during hard acceleration, air routing changes by itself, it's probably due to a leak in the system or a faulty check valve in the vacuum reservoir. A complaint that the mode shifts from the dash to the floor at wide open throttle is evidence that the system isn't holding vacuum.

9. The correct answer is A. If the engine is started while pressure testing a cooling system and the pressure immediately increases, there could be a head gasket leak, but not into the crankcase. The coolant may be going out the tailpipe, but since this is a late model gasoline engine vehicle and equipped with a catalytic converter, there is no white smoke from the exhaust because the converter super-heats the coolant into such a fine vapor that it is not noticeable.

10. The correct answer is A. Systems using an expansion valve have a receiver/drier between the valve and condenser, while orifice tube systems have an accumulator between the evaporator and compressor. Technician B is wrong because on R134a systems, the low side service port is the smaller one.

11. The correct answer is B. If the system reacts with a change to one or two inputs but not to the third, the problem is most likely confined to the single sensor or its circuit. But if no reaction is observed on any of the units, or only a partial reaction is seen, the problem is usually with the programmer.

12. The correct answer is C. When removing the orifice tube with an extractor tool, do not twist or rotate the orifice tube in the line as it can break. If an orifice tube breaks during removal, special tools are available to extract broken orifice tubes. All of the other answers are methods of orifice tube replacement.

13. The correct answer is D. When charging a retrofitted system with R134a refrigerant, the system will only require 80-90 percent of the original R12 charge amount.

14. The correct answer is B. Technician A is wrong because propane gas leak detectors cannot detect R134a. Technician B is right, but he must make sure the electronic leak detector is designed for R134a, as many older units are not.

15. The correct answer is C. Desiccants are not universal and different types must be used with different refrigerants and lubricating oils. When a system is retrofitted, the replacement receiver/drier or accumulator has XH-7 or XH-9 desiccant.

16. The correct answer is B. Technician A is wrong because if the clutch coil was defective, the compressor clutch would not engage. Technician B is correct because, since the compressor clutch engages when 12 volts is directly applied, the problem is in the compressor control circuit, which includes the pressure cycling switch.

17. The correct answer is A. Fogged windows that smear when wiped and moisture on the passenger floor are telltale signs of a leaking heater core. Technician B is incorrect because, while a clogged evaporator case drain could cause the case to fill up with moisture and spill out onto the floor, it would not cause a slimy film on the windows.

18. The correct answer is C, both technicians. Knocking noises from the compressor usually indicate internal damage, especially on piston-type compressors. However, always check the compressor mounting and brackets before condemning the compressor for noise. A loose mounting can cause knocking noises from the compressor area that may be mistaken for internal compressor noise.

19. The correct answer is D. A stuck open heater control valve could cause problems when heat is not wanted, but because coolant flow to the heater core is not interrupted, the heater valve would not cause poor heater performance. A defective temperature blend door actuator could cause poor heat if the blend door was stuck in the wrong position. Radiator coolant temperature below 150°F (66°C) would indicate a missing or stuck open thermostat, which could also cause poor heater performance. A heater core return hose that is much cooler than the inlet hose means that the heater core is plugged or air bound, also causing poor heat.

20. The correct answer is D. Although the air temperature at the center outlet would be about the same, if the condenser is plugged, the manifold gauge readings would be high. All of the other answers are possible causes for the symptoms in the question.

21. The correct answer is B. There must be at least 50 psi of refrigerant pressure in the system in order for a leak detector to be able to sense a leak. Refrigerant may have to be added to the system to achieve this.

22. The correct answer is A. During a retrofit, the new R134a service fittings are usually conversion fittings that are installed on the existing R12 fittings. Technician B is wrong because if the R12 fittings are not converted, they must be permanently capped.

23. The correct answer is B. Most temperature sensors can be tested for resistance and voltage drop. In general, the sensor should be replaced if its resistance is not within specification. Since a temperature sensor's resistance varies with temperature, check the sensor voltage against temperature and compare to manufacturer's specifications.

24. The correct answer is C, both technicians. Technician A is correct because the high-pressure cutout switch should break the circuit to the compressor clutch if it detects pressures above a preset level. If the compressor continues to run when pressure passes the threshold of the switch calibration, the switch is defective. Technician B is also right because an obstruction to air flow through the condenser can cause excessive high side pressure.

25. The correct answer is C. During operation, the clutch may cycle on and off several times each minute. Insufficient refrigerant causes rapid change in heat load on the evaporator, which affects system pressures. If the clutch cycles rapidly, it may be a sign of low refrigerant charge. A defective thermostatic switch may not be engaging the compressor clutch long enough. The thermostatic switch has a capillary tube attached to the evaporator outlet or inserted between the evaporator core fins to sense the temperature. This capillary is attached to a switch that opens and closes, as necessary, to cycle the compressor.

26. The correct answer is D. To properly evacuate an A/C system, the vacuum pump should be operated for a minimum of 30 minutes.

Answers to Study-Guide Test Questions

27. The correct answer is B. Technician A is wrong because a special tool is only required to disconnect spring lock fittings.

28. The correct answer is D. There are filters that fit into both the high and low sides of the system. All of the other statements ate true concerning in-line filters.

29. The correct answer is C, both technicians. If there is foam, the charge is low, but if there are only a couple of bubbles, it is probably OK. A few bubbles when the compressor cycles on is normal. Oil streaks in the sight glass usually indicate a low charge and that the compressor is pumping oil from its sump.

30. The correct answer is C. Moisture in the A/C system can ice up in the expansion valve and block refrigerant flow. On systems with R12, moisture can combine with the chlorine in the R12 to form hydrochloric acid. These chemicals can corrode metals and attack rubber parts.

31. The correct answer is D. A disengaged clutch type radiator fan would not cause low heater output. All of the other answers are possible causes of low heater output.

32. The correct answer is D. A broken compressor reed valve could not cause the high side pressure to be above specifications.

33. The correct answer is B. To prevent overfilling during transfer of refrigerant, never fill a container to more than 60 percent of its gross weight rating.

34. The correct answer is B. Regardless of what condition the door is in, the key here is that the gauge reading is zero, meaning there is a vacuum leak in the actuator.

35. The correct answer is C, both technicians. If the drain at the bottom of the evaporator case becomes clogged and water collects and stagnates, or if the surface of the evaporator remains too moist due to high humidity, bacteria can grow in the stagnant water or on the evaporator surface and cause an odor. This odor is then sent into the passenger compartment by the blower motor.

36. The correct answer is C, both technicians. A clicking or buzzing noise coming from the compressor is a sign that the system is overcharged and liquid refrigerant is entering the compressor. Unless some refrigerant is removed, severe compressor damage may result. This noise could also result from air in the system.

37. The correct answer is A. The power steering pressure switch is installed in the power steering system and reports on high pressure conditions caused by a load being placed on the engine by the power steering pump. The computer may decide to temporarily shut down the compressor to prevent engine stalling or low idle speed, or it could also raise idle speed through control of an idle speed control device. During parallel parking maneuvers, the steering wheel is most likely being moved to full lock at some point, increasing pressure. Technician A is right because, if this increased pressure is not being communicated to the computer by the switch, the A/C compressor will continue to run with its load on the engine or the idle speed will not be raised enough to keep the engine from stalling. Technician B is wrong because if the problem was with the power steering pump, the stalling would occur regardless of whether the A/C was on.

38. The correct answer is C. The receiver/drier is located in the high side of the system, between the condenser and evaporator, ahead of the expansion valve. It stores liquid refrigerant until needed by the evaporator. The accumulator is the component that keeps liquid refrigerant from entering the compressor, but accumulators are used in systems with orifice tubes, not expansion valves.

39. The correct answer is A. The pressure cycling switch senses the low side pressure near the evaporator outlet and is usually found on the accumulator. Technician B is wrong because the switch is often mounted in a Schrader fitting so it can be replaced without the loss of refrigerant.

40. The correct answer is C, both technicians. Charging the system can be performed through either the high side or low side when the engine is not running, but must be done only through the low side when the engine is running. This safety measure prevents high side pressure from entering the refrigerant container and possibly causing an explosion.

41. The correct answer is C. The purpose of the low pressure cutoff switch is compressor protection. The compressor clutch circuit is opened if the pressure in the system drops too low. This would be an indication that the system has lost some or all of its refrigerant charge. Since the lubricating oil is carried by the refrigerant, a loss could cause damage to the compressor if it were allowed to operate without sufficient lubrication.

42. The correct answer is B. To purge the air, connect the tank to the recovery/recycling machine and slowly vent the air vapor from the top of the container. Continue venting until the pressure falls below the limit shown on your chart. If the pressure inside the container still exceeds the pressure limit shown, recycle the entire contents. Technician B is wrong because the container must be stored for 12 hours, not eight.

43. The correct answer is C. The thermostatic switch, which is used to cycle the A/C compressor on and off, depends on the temperature of the evaporator in order to operate.

44. The correct answer is D. A properly operating clutch should stop the fan from spinning within two seconds after a hot engine shut down. All of the other answers are indications of a defective fan clutch.

45. The correct answer is C, both technicians. In non-ATC systems, the function of the ambient temperature switch is to inhibit compressor clutch operation in cold ambient temperatures. This function mainly protects the compressor from poor or no lubrication, which could be the result of cold refrigerant oil. In ATC systems, the ambient temperature sensor senses ambient outside temperature. As ambient or interior temperatures stray, the sensors pick up the change and the system adjusts the outlet duct temperature accordingly to compensate for the temperature changes.

46. The correct answer is B. Expansion valves are usually spring loaded devices with a diaphragm that is linked to a plunger. Without any pressure against the diaphragm from the gas in the capillary tube, the spring inside the expansion valve would cause the valve to stick closed.

47. The correct answer is B. If both hoses leading to the heater core are hot, coolant is circulating through the heater core. One hose that is significantly cooler than the other would indicate a clogged heater core. However, if the temperature control cable is incorrectly adjusted, the temperature blend door may not allow enough warm air to enter the passenger compartment for sufficient heating.

48. The correct answer is B. The parts used during a retrofit don't necessarily have to come from a kit and even if they do, that information is not required on the retrofit label. All of the other information is required to be listed.

49. The correct answer is B. Fault codes usually only indicate which circuit the problem is in; they don't necessarily indicate which component in the circuit has failed. The problem could be caused by a loose connection, improper modification, or a broken wire, so perform a thorough inspection when diagnosing a malfunction. Ensure that all grounds are clean and making good contact. If basic mechanical and electrical checks fail to locate the problem, follow manufacturer's electronic system test procedures.

50. The correct answer is C. The release of CFCs into the atmosphere has been found to be a major cause of ozone layer depletion.

51. The correct answer is C. The sunload sensor is a photovoltaic diode. All of the other sensors listed are NTC thermistors.

52. The correct answer is B. Answer A is wrong because the fan control resistor does not affect high speed fan operation. Answer C is wrong because a short to ground here will blow the 20-amp fuse and neither fan will work. Answer D is wrong because if the 60-amp fuse is blown, neither fan will work.

53. The correct answer is D. If there is an open in circuit 15 between the 15/15S splice and the fan motor, the motor will not run at all. All of the other answers are possible causes for no low speed blower motor operation.

Answers to Study-Guide Test Questions

54. The correct answer is D, neither technician is correct. Both technicians are jumping to conclusions. To a find the problem, a logical diagnostic procedure must be followed or parts may be replaced unnecessarily. This includes performing a preliminary inspection of the A/C system and checking refrigerant pressures before condemning any part of the ATC system.

55. The correct answer is A. The high-pressure cutout switch is normally closed. It opens the compressor clutch circuit when high side pressures are excessive in order to protect the compressor. All of the other answers would cause the compressor clutch not to engage.

56. The correct answer is C, both technicians are correct. The in-vehicle temperature sensor is located in the aspirator, which is located in the dashboard. The aspirator tube is connected to a heater-A/C duct. The air flowing in the duct past the tube creates a vacuum, drawing in-vehicle air past the sensor. If there is an obstruction in the aspirator tube or the tube is disconnected from the duct, air will not be drawn past the in-vehicle temperature sensor and the sensor will not be able to accurately measure the temperature inside the vehicle. This could account for the discrepancy between the temperature setting and the actual temperature inside the vehicle.

57. The correct answer is B. The ambient temperature sensor is an NTC (Negative Temperature Coefficient) thermistor. When an NTC thermistor is heated, the resistance should drop, and when it is cooled, resistance should increase.

58. The correct answer is A. Technician B is wrong because if there is an open between the P/BL and P/O splice and the motor, the motor will not run at all.

59. The correct answer is A. An open thermal limiter would prevent the blower motor from working on any speed but high. The other answers are incorrect because any of these causes would prevent the blower motor from working at all.

60. The correct answer is B. A faulty A/C damper door switch or a problem in the circuit between the switch and the A/C clutch cycling switch could be the problem. Since the test light showed that there is power going to the A/C damper door switch, all of the other components listed are OK.

NOTES

Glossary of Terms

accumulator - a component used to store or hold liquid refrigerant in an air conditioning system that also contains a desiccant.

actuator - a control device that delivers mechanical action in response to a vacuum or electrical signal.

air conditioning (A/C) - a system that cools and dehumidifies the air entering the passenger compartment of a vehicle.

air ducts - tubes, channels or other tubular structures used to carry air to a specific location.

air gap - the space or gap between the compressor drive hub and pulley assembly.

ambient temperature - the temperature of the air surrounding an object.

ambient temperature switch - a switch that prevents air conditioner operation below a certain ambient temperature.

amplifier - a circuit or device used to increase the voltage or current of a signal.

antifreeze - a material such as ethylene glycol which is added to water to lower its freezing point; used in an automobile's cooling system.

atmospheric pressure - the weight of the air at sea level (14.7 lbs. per sq. in.) or at higher altitudes.

automatic temperature control (ATC) system - a climate control system that uses the heating and air conditioning systems to maintain the interior temperature selected by the vehicle's passengers.

axial - having the same direction or being parallel to the axis or rotation.

blend door - a door in the heating and air conditioning system that controls the temperature of the air going into the passenger compartment.

blower motor - the electric motor which drives the fan that circulates air inside the vehicle passenger compartment.

boiling point - the temperature at which a liquid turns to vapor.

British Thermal Unit (BTU) - a unit of measurement; the amount of heat that is required to raise the temperature of one pound of water by one degree F.

capillary tube - a thin, gas-filled tube that senses the temperature of the evaporator and relays this information to the thermostat and/or expansion valve.

Celsius - the basis of the metric system of temperature measurement in which water's boiling point is 100°C and its freezing point is 0°C.

charge - to fill, or bring up to the specific level, an A/C system with refrigerant; the required amount of refrigerant for an A/C system.

chlorofluorocarbon (CFC) - any organic chemical compounds made up of carbon, chlorine and fluorine atoms, usually used in refrigeration. R12 is a CFC.

clutch cycling switch - a device that opens and closes the circuit that engages the air conditioning compressor clutch based on pressure or temperature.

compressor - an engine driven device that compresses refrigerant gas and pumps it through the air conditioning system.

condensation - the process of a vapor becoming a liquid; the opposite of evaporation.

condense - to cool a vapor to below its boiling point, where it then condenses into a liquid.

condenser - a device, similar to a radiator, in which the refrigerant loses heat and changes state from a high pressure gas to a high pressure liquid as it dissipates heat to the surrounding air.

coolant - a mixture of water and ethylene glycol based antifreeze that circulates through the engine to help maintain proper temperatures.

cooling fan - a mechanically or electrically driven propeller that draws air through the radiator.

cooling system - the system used to remove excess heat from an engine and transfer it to the atmosphere. Includes the radiator, cooling fan, hoses, water pump, thermostat and engine coolant passages.

core - in automotive terminology, the main part of a heat exchanger, such as a radiator, evaporator or heater. Usually made of tubes, surrounded by cooling fins, used to transfer heat from the coolant to the air.

corrosion - the eating into or wearing away of a substance gradually by rusting or chemical action.

crossflow radiator - a radiator in which coolant enters on one side, travels through tubes, and collects on the opposite side (see **downflow radiator**).

cycling clutch system - an A/C system that controls temperature by switching the compressor clutch on and off.

--d--

deflection - a turning aside, bending or deviation; bending or movement away from the normal position due to loading.

degree - used to designate temperature readings or 1 degree as a 1/360 part of a circle.

dehumidify - to remove moisture (humidity) from the air.

desiccant - any hygroscopic material that removes and traps moisture, usually found in a bag in the accumulator or receiver/drier in air conditioning systems.

diagnostic trouble code (DTC) - a code that represents and can be used to identify a malfunction in a computer control system.

diaphragm - a flexible, impermeable membrane on which pressure acts to produce mechanical movement.

diode - a simple semiconductor device that permits flow of electricity in one direction but not the other.

discharge - to remove the refrigerant from an air conditioning system.

displacement - the volume the cylinder holds between the top dead center and bottom dead center positions of the piston.

downflow radiator - a radiator in which coolant enters the top of the radiator and is drawn downward by gravity (see **crossflow radiator**).

--e--

electromagnet - a magnet formed by electrical flow through a conductor.

electromagnetic induction - moving a wire through a magnetic field to create current flow in the wire.

electromechanical - refers to a device that incorporates both electrical and mechanical principles together in its operation.

electronic - pertaining to the control of systems or devices by the use of small electrical signals and various semiconductor devices and circuits.

electronic control module (ECM) - the computer in an electronic control system, also known as an electronic control unit (ECU).

engine coolant temperature (ECT) sensor - a sensor which works by a negative coefficient thermistor that loses resistance as its temperature goes up (just like the intake air temperature sensor). When the computer applies its 5-volt reference signal to the sensor, this voltage is reduced through a ground circuit by an amount corresponding to the temperature of the engine coolant.

evacuate - the process of applying vacuum to a closed refrigeration system to remove air and moisture.

evaporation - the process through which a liquid is turned into vapor.

evaporator - a heat exchanger, in which low-pressure refrigerant flows and changes state, absorbing heat from the surrounding air.

Glossary of Terms

--f--

Fahrenheit - a scale of temperature measurement with the boiling point of water at 212°F. In the metric system, water's boiling point is 100°Celsius.

fan - a mechanically or electrically driven propeller that draws or pushes air through the radiator, condenser, heater core or evaporator core.

fan clutch - a device attached to a mechanically driven cooling fan that allows the fan to freewheel when the engine is cold or the vehicle is driven at speed.

fan shroud - an enclosure that routes air through the radiator cooling fins.

Freon - DuPont registered trade name for R12 refrigerant (dichlorodifluoromethane).

--g--

gauge set - the set of gauges that attaches to the high and low side of the A/C system and is used for diagnosis. Also called a manifold gauge set.

ground - the negatively charged side of a circuit. A ground can be a wire, the negative side of the battery or the vehicle chassis.

--h--

head pressure - the pressure of the refrigerant at the compressor outlet.

heater core - a radiator-like device used to heat the inside of a vehicle. Hot coolant is pumped through it by the water pump, and heat from the coolant moves from the heater core to the passenger compartment as the blower fan forces air through it.

high side - the high-pressure half of an A/C system, usually refers to all components between the compressor outlet and the expansion valve or orifice tube.

--l--

latent heat of condensation - the amount of heat given off as a vapor changes state from a gas to a liquid without the temperature changing.

latent heat of evaporation - the amount of heat needed for a liquid to change state to a vapor without the temperature changing.

leak detector - a tool used to locate refrigerant leaks.

liquid line - the tube and/or hose leading from the outlet of the condenser to the expansion valve or orifice tube.

low side - the suction side of an A/C system between the evaporator core inlet (after the expansion valve or orifice tube) and the compressor.

lubrication - reducing friction between moving parts.

--m--

magnet - any body with the property of attracting iron or steel.

magnetic field - the areas surrounding the poles of a magnet which are affected by its forces of attraction or repulsion.

microprocessor - the portion of a microcomputer that receives sensor input and handles all calculations.

multimeter - a tool that combines the functions of a voltmeter, ohmmeter and ammeter together in one diagnostic instrument.

--n--

negative temperature coefficient thermistor - a thermistor which loses electrical resistance as it gets warmer. The temperature sensors for the computer control system are negative temperature coefficient thermistors. The effect is to systematically lower the 5-volt reference voltage sent them by the computer, yielding a signal that corresponds to the temperature of the measured source. Typically the ECT and IAT sensors use this principle.

--o--

ohm - a unit of measured electrical resistance.

open circuit - electrical circuit that has an intentional (switch) or unintentional (bad connection) break in the wire.

orifice - a precisely sized hole that controls the flow of fluid.

orifice tube - used in some air conditioning systems, a component with a fixed opening through which refrigerant passes as it is metered into the evaporator core. Also called an expansion tube.

--p--

polyalkyline glycol (PAG) oil - lubricant used with A/C systems containing R-134a refrigerant.

pressure - the exertion of force upon a body. Pressure is developed within the cooling or A/C system and is measured in pounds per square inch on a gauge.

psi - measurement of pressure in pounds per square inch.

--r--

R12 - the generic term for CFC refrigerant used in older A/C systems. Also called Freon.

R134a - generic term for a modern refrigerant that does not contain CFCs and does not harm the ozone layer.

radiator - the part of the cooling system that acts as a heat exchanger, transferring heat to atmosphere. It consists of a core and holding tanks connected to the cooling system by hoses.

radiator cap - a device that seals the radiator and maintains a set pressure in the cooling system.

receiver/drier - an A/C system component into which high-pressure liquid refrigerant flows and is temporarily stored and dehydrated, usually located between the condenser outlet and expansion valve.

reclaim - to send refrigerant to an off-site facility where it is restored to its original purity so that it may be reused.

reciprocating - an up-and-down or back-and-forth motion.

recover - to remove refrigerant from a system and store it temporarily.

recycle - to remove contaminants such as moisture, particulates, etc. from refrigerant and reintroduce the refrigerant into the A/C system.

refrigerant - a chemical compound used in an A/C system to remove heat from the evaporator and transfer it to the condenser.

refrigerant cycle - the complete loop or circuit that refrigerant passes through as it changes state from a vapor, to a liquid, then back to a vapor.

refrigerant oil - either a mineral or synthetic oil designed specifically for A/C systems.

relay - an electromagnetic switch that uses low amperage current to control a circuit with high amperage.

residual pressure - remaining or leftover pressure.

residue - surplus; what remains after a separation.

resistance - the opposition offered by a substance or body to the passage of electric current through it.

retrofit - to convert an older A/C system that used R12 to use R134a refrigerant, usually by replacing various components.

rotary - refers to a circular motion.

--s--

schrader valve - a spring operated valve used to open and close the service outlets in an A/C system. They are the service valves used to attach manifold gauges and to charge or evacuate the system.

service port - any of the various designs of fittings that allow service tools such as manifold gauges to be attached to an A/C system (see also **schrader valve**).

servo - a device, such as an electric motor or hydraulic piston, that is controlled by an amplified signal from a low power command device.

Glossary of Terms

sight glass - a window in the high pressure side of the A/C system, usually in the receiver/drier, to observe the refrigerant for signs of bubbles and/or moisture.

serpentine belt - multiple ribbed belts that wrap around and drive various engine mounted components.

slip - condition caused when a driving part rotates faster than a driven part.

suction - suction exists in a vessel when the pressure is lower than the atmospheric pressure.

suction line - the low side tube and/or hose leading from the evaporator core outlet to the compressor inlet.

superheat - the addition of more heat to a gas after it has already vaporized; the heat added to vaporized refrigerant after it has changed state from a liquid to a gas.

superheat switch - a switch, usually mounted on the compressor on certain A/C systems that completes the circuit to the thermal limiter switch.

--t--

technical service bulletin (TSB) - information published by vehicle manufacturers that describes updated service procedures and service procedures that should be used to handle vehicle defects.

tension - effort that elongates or stretches material.

thermal limiter - a component, similar to a fuse, which blows to open the compressor clutch circuit when the superheat switch detects low A/C system pressure.

thermistor - A temperature sensitive variable resistor in which the resistance decreases as its temperature increases.

thermostat - a device installed in the cooling system that allows the engine to come to operating temperature quickly and then maintain a minimum operating temperature.

thermostatic expansion valve (TXV) - used on some air conditioning systems, a temperature sensitive device that meters the flow of refrigerant into the evaporator core. Also called an expansion valve.

--v--

vapor - a substance in a gaseous state. Liquid becomes vapor when brought above the boiling point.

volt - a unit of measurement of electromotive force. One volt of electromotive force applied steadily to a conductor of one ohm resistance produces a current of one ampere.

voltage drop - voltage lost by the passage of electrical current through resistance.

voltmeter - a tool used to measure the voltage available at any point in an electrical system.

--w--

water pump - device used to circulate coolant through the engine.

water valve - a device used to control the flow of hot coolant to the heater core, operated electrically, by cable, or by vacuum.

NOTES

NOTES